GLADIATORS
GAME BOOK No.1

TM © LWT Programmes Ltd. 1992

TM

Stan Nicholls

B▣XTREE

First published in the UK 1992
by BOXTREE LIMITED, Broadwall House,
21 Broadwall, London SE1 9PL

10 9 8 7 6 5 4 3 2

Cover design: Head
Typeset by Spectrum Typesetting Ltd., London
Printed and bound by Cox & Wyman, Reading, Berkshire

1-85283-865-5

A catalogue record for this book is available from the
British Library

CONTENTS

INTRODUCTION

Over the past three years, *American Gladiators* has been a smash hit on US television. For LWT's sensational British version of the show a totally new set of Gladiators has been chosen. Twelve super-fit men and women, carefully selected for their athletic prowess, stand ready to battle all-comers in trials of strength, skill, speed, wits and stamina.

Auditions were held around the country to find sportsmen and women capable of facing the Gladiators in a series of gruelling televised events. Only a few proved good enough to tackle the demands of *Atlaspheres, The Wall, Danger Zone, Swingshot, Hang Tough* and *Duel*. And those managing to survive these half-dozen ordeals, pitted every step of the way against Gladiators dedicated to stopping them, then confronted the fiendish *Eliminator*.

Do *you* have what it takes to become a Gladiator Champion?

In the following pages you will experience all the action and excitement of *Gladiators* as a contender. You can choose one Gladiator to oppose you through all the events or pick a new foe for each. You can work your way through the events alone or play alongside friends and compare your scores.

SHADOW, SCORPIO, WARRIOR, JET, SARACEN, PHOENIX, HAWK, PANTHER, WOLF, FLAME, COBRA and LIGHTNING await your challenge.

Study carefully the following descriptions of the twelve Gladiators, which include their individual strengths, weaknesses and special abilities. The decisions you make when entering the events will depend on knowing what your Gladiator opponent is capable of.

MEET THE GLADIATORS

(1) SHADOW

Height: 6′4″ (192cm) *Weight*: 19st (121.1kg)
Strengths: Weight; Strength; Rationality; A strategist
Best events: Atlaspheres ★★★ Duel (unbeaten) ★★★ Hang Tough ★★
Behind the Mask:
- Gladiators' team leader
- 15 years hard fitness training added 7 stone to his weight
- Excels in track and field events, American football, bodybuilding
- Eats 10 chicken pieces per day
- 1978-80 Teenage Mr Britain; 1982 Novice Mr Britain; 1989 British Weightlifting team, Moscow: 2nd

(2) SCORPIO

Height: 5′9″ (175cm) *Weight*: 9st 7lb (60.3kg)
Strengths: Intelligence; Agility
Best events: The Wall ★★★
Behind the Mask:
- Talented gymnast
- High jump champion
- Keeps super-fit with weight training, aerobics, horse riding
- Honours degree from Guildhall School of Drama
- Film credits: *Slipstream, Mountains of the Moon, Meaning of Life*.

(3) **WARRIOR**

Height: 6'5" (175cm) *Weight*: 21st 4lb (130.9kg)
Strengths: Will never give up in combat; Enormous size and strength; All-rounder
Best events: Duel ★★★ Atlaspheres ★★
Behind the Mask:
- Bodybuilding for 7 years
- Lost 2 stone for *Gladiators* to increase his agility
- Cycling, running, and aerobics part of his regime
- Ex-Rugby League/Rugby Union player
- Junior British Decathlon champion
- Competed for the Mr Universe title

(4) **JET**

Height: 5'7" (170cm) *Weight*: 10st (63.5kg)
Strengths: All-rounder; Speed; Flexibility & agility
Best events: The Wall ★★★ Swingshot ★★★ Hang Tough ★★ Duel ★★★
Behind the Mask:
- Health and fitness teacher
- Professional dancer and actress
- Former national gymnast squad member
- Advises on nutrition and lifestyle
- Keen runner and hill walker

(5) **SARACEN**

Height: 6'3" (190cm) *Weight*: 17st (108kg)
Strengths: Enjoys combat; Tenacity; Muscle power
Best events: Hang Tough ★★★ The Wall ★★
Behind the Mask:
- Competed as a bodybuilder
- Wants Mr Olympia title
- Strict weight training regime, concentrates on different part of body each day
- Gym circuit work and athletics part of his routine

(6) PHOENIX

Height: 5'7" (170cm) *Weight*: 9st 5lb (59.4kg)
Strengths: Muscle power; Expert Thai/kick boxer; Light in weight; Agile and fast
Best events: The Wall ★★★ Swingshot ★★
Behind the Mask:
- Bodybuilding Miss UK 1990-1
- Miss Oscars 1991
- Competed in NABBA Miss Figure and Miss Universe
- Featured in TV documentary on feminine side of bodybuilding
- Has just released first single

(7) HAWK

Height: 6'1" (185cm) *Weight*: 17st (108kg)
Strengths: Agility; Intelligence; Stamina
Best events: Hang Tough ★★★ Swingshot ★★★
Behind the Mask:
- Rugby player and boxer
- Represented Cardiff Amateur Athletics Club at long jump
- Keen cyclist
- Ex-Mr Wales
- Left school with 2 'A' levels, planning to teach

(8) PANTHER

Height: 5'6" (168cm) *Weight*: 9st 7lb (60.3kg)
Strengths: Muscle power; Strength in lower body; Endurance
Best events: Atlaspheres ★★★
Behind the Mask:
- Dedicated bodybuilder: has 22" thighs and 13" biceps
- Competed in track and field events
- Miss Britain, Miss Europe, Miss Universe 1991 bodybuilding titles; Miss Russia 1992

(9) **WOLF**

Height: 6' (183cm) *Weight*: 16st (101.6kg)
Strengths: Agility; Expert kick boxer; Strong build
Best events: Hang Tough ★★★ Swingshot ★★★ Wall ★★★
Behind the Mask:
- Trains 5 days a week
- Consumes 5000 calories a day in 6 small meals
- Expert snowboarder and rollerblade skater
- The bad boy of the Gladiators keeps a pet goldfish!

(10) **FLAME**

Height: 6' (183cm) *Weight*: 10st (63.5kg)
Strengths: Stamina; Height; Timing; Upper body strength; speed
Best events: Swingshot ★★★ Duel ★★ Hang Tough ★★
Behind the Mask:
- An American who has played basketball, and swum competitively
- Competed in track and field events
- Keen on dance, jogging, skiing, and aerobic exercise

(11) **COBRA**

Height: 6' (183cm) *Weight*: 15st (95.7kg)
Strengths: Martial arts expert; Flexibility; Speed; Strategist
Best events: Hang Tough ★★★ Duel ★★★
Behind the Mask:
- His trademark: high kicks
- Nicknamed 'Snake Hips': he slithers between the hoops of Hang Tough
- Works as engineer
- Dedicated bodybuilder

(12) LIGHTNING

Height: 5'7" (170cm) *Weight*: 9st 5lb (59.4kg)
Strengths: Speed; Flexibility; Agility and timing
Best events: Atlaspheres ★★★ Hang Tough ★★★
Swingshot ★★
Behind the Mask:
- A gymnast who has won 23 gold medals
- Daily aerobic and weight training
- Keen runner
- Dedicated bodybuilder

HOW TO SELECT YOUR OPPONENT

Toss a coin.

If the result is heads:
Throw a die. The number you get will be your gladiator opponent number.

If the result is tails:
Throw a die. Add six to the number you get. Match the result with the appropraite Gladiator number.

THE EVENTS

INTRODUCTION

Now that your Gladiator opponent has been chosen, you are ready to compete in ATLASPHERES, THE WALL, DANGER ZONE, SWINGSHOT, HANG TOUGH, DUEL and ELIMINATOR.

You have the choice of either staying with the same Gladiator through all the first six events or picking a different Gladiator to battle in each one.

After the event has been described you are presented with four **Principal Options**. These represent four alternative ways of playing the event. Study the abilities of the Gladiator opponent you have drawn before selecting your **Principal Option**.

Each **Principal Option** leads you to a set of three **Intermediate Options**. These represent an incident, mishap or other response to your **Principal Option**. The incident is described, then you choose one of the offered ways to proceed with the event. You must stay with this choice.

Each event is scored at the end. Add up all your scores from the first six events before moving on to ELIMINATOR.

ELIMINATOR does not include a Gladiator opponent – you are on your own. As you will see, this event has a different structure, and the points you have accumulated in the six events before it determine how well you do in this final game.

You now have all the information you need to begin playing against the Gladiators.

(1) ATLASPHERES

Body strength and endurance, and the ability to make rational decisions could prove vital in this punishing event.

You have been placed inside a red and yellow metal sphere, seven foot in diameter. The sphere acts as a kind of rigid exo-skeleton and you can see out of it through the framework. You power your way around the arena by walking inside the sphere, steadying yourself with your arms. The strain on your legs and back is intense and if you fall you may never regain your balance.

The object is to roll your sphere into as many of the four scoring pods set into the playing floor as you can. Each time you place your sphere over a pod, you gain points. The pods issue a plume of CO_2 if the sensor in the middle is struck. Three points are scored for every hit.

In your way is your Gladiator opponent, competing in a silver-coloured ball of their own. The aim: to prevent you getting near the pods and scoring any points.

Contenders cannot go straight to the pod nearest the bottom of the ramp leading into the playing area. Nor are they allowed to go back to the same pod they have just activated unless they've been hit by the Gladiator.

PRINCIPAL OPTIONS

Choose one of the following options carefully.

Do you:

a) *Go for the direct approach, relying on pure strength and single-mindedness to push aside your Gladiator foe?*

b) *Try to confuse your opponent by appearing to make for a particular pod then swerving at the last moment and heading for another?*

c)   *Roll your sphere at random around the playing floor until you spot an opening, then make for the undefended pod?*

d)   *Attempt to out-pace your opponent by racing him or her to the pods, hoping your speed will be the greater?*

INTERMEDIATE OPTIONS

Having chosen one of the **Principal Options** on the previous page you are now presented with a set of **Intermediate Options**. Each **Principal Option** corresponds to three **Intermediate Options**.

Intermediate options contain responses to a particular incident, crisis or mishap arising during the event. These incidents are described. Then you have to pick one of three ways of dealing with it.

For example, if you chose **Principal Option** a) for AT-LASPHERES, you may decide that **Intermediate Option** 1) is the best way of solving the problem that has arisen. You must therefore abide by the course of action outlined in number 1 in the P.O. a) section below.

P.O. a) What happens:

You have underestimated the strength of your Gladiator opponent. The way to your chosen pod is blocked and time is running out.

In response, you:

1. Continue to batter away at the Gladiator with the aim of wearing him/her down.

2. Pull away and make for the next nearest pod in the hope of out-racing your opponent.

3. Pretend to move towards a pod on the other side of the playing floor then, with your Gladiator in pursuit, make an unexpected turn and go all out for another pod.

P.O. b) What happens:

In trying to confuse your opponent you use too much energy. You may not have enough strength left to fight him off when you reach a pod.

In response, you:

1. Make for the nearest pod in the hope of having enough strength in reserve to power the Gladiator out of your way.

2. Set a course for a distant pod and race towards it as fast as you can in a bid to out-speed your Gladiator opponent.

3. Go on the offensive by using precious strength to crash your sphere into the Gladiator's, hoping this will disorientate him long enough for you to get to a pod.

P.O. c) What happens:

The Gladiator spoils your play by following you closely from the moment the event begins. The seconds are flying by and you cannot find an opening.

In response, you:

1. Put every last ounce of your strength into breaking away from your opponent and dashing for a pod.

2. Continue to roll your sphere around randomly in the hope the Gladiator will tire or have a lapse of concentration you can exploit.

3. Attempt a trial of strength with your opponent in a bid to smash them aside.

P.O. d) What happens:

You stumble and temporarily lose control of your sphere.

In response, you:

1. Struggle to regain control with the intention of still trying to out-run your opponent.

2. Resign yourself to not being able to beat the Gladiator in

a straight race and prepare to fend off his attack.

3. Pit your mind and body to the task of powering past your foe in the hope you are stronger.

Event One
ATLASPHERES
SCORE CHECK

Look up your Gladiator opponent's entry, then check which Principal and Intermediate Options you chose.

 ### (1) SHADOW
Atlaspheres is one of SHADOW's best events. He is the Gladiators' cool-headed team leader, and fares best at events requiring strength rather than speed.

SHADOW is unlikely to be fooled by options designed to confuse him, but you could out-pace him if you have sufficient reserves of strength and good muscular power. He is most likely to best you when it comes to straightforward trials of strength.

Bearing this in mind, this is how you scored against SHADOW in Atlaspheres.

PRINCIPAL OPTION a)
Intermediate Options 1-3:

1: You are unlikely to overwhelm his strength; 2: Out-pacing him is your best chance; 3: Odds are even that he would fall for a confusion ploy.

SCORES 1: 10 points. 2: 30 points. 3: 20 points.

b) 1-3:

1: Few people have as much reserve power as SHADOW; 2: You could out-run him; 3: He may be temporarily disoriented if you move fast.

SCORES 1: 10 points. 2: 30 points. 3: 20 points.

c) 1-3:

1: Speed is the best option, *if* you can get away; 2: He won't tire but could be caught unawares; 3: No way.

SCORES 1: 30 points. 2: 20 points. 3: 10 points.

d) 1-3:

1: Good option if you regain control fast; 2: Best you can hope for is a stalemate; 3: It's possible, remotely.

SCORES 1: 30 points. 2: 10 points. 3: 20 points.

---

(2) SCORPIO

SCORPIO fares best at those events requiring agility. She weight-trains and has a good strength level, but is more likely to excel in games where speed and subtlety of movement count.

SCORPIO is hard to out-run or out-manoeuvre. But in some circumstances she can be bettered in head-on power contests. Options meant to throw her off have a reasonable chance of succeeding.

PRINCIPAL OPTION a)
Intermediate Options 1-3:

1: You may be able to wear her down, if you can catch her; 2: Odds are she would win a straight race; 3: Could work, but remember she is fast.

SCORES 1: 30 points. 2: 10 points. 3: 20 points.

b) 1-3:

1: You have a good chance of achieving this; 2: Her speed and dexterity tell here; 3: A strength trial favours you.

SCORES 1: 30 points. 2: 10 points. 3: 20 points.

c) 1-3:

1: You may break away, but SCORPIO could score dash-wise. 2: Unlikely to tire, a break in concentration is possible. 3: You could overpower her.

SCORES 1: 10 points. 2: 20 points. 3: 30 points.

d) 1-3:

1: Her speed and your precious time loss puts you at a disadvantage. 2: Odds just in favour of you beating her off. 3: You could overcome her in the long-haul.

SCORES 1: 10 points. 2: 20 points. 3: 30 points

---

(3) WARRIOR

At twenty-one and a half stone and six foot five, it comes as no surprise that WARRIOR tends to do best in the strength-related events, and Atlaspheres is one of his specialities. But he is more than just a muscled power-house. His training regime includes aerobics and cycling and running, making for an agility surprising in a man of his size.

PRINCIPAL OPTION a)
Intermediate Options 1-3:

1: Are you *kidding*? 2: Unless you weigh more than WARRIOR you could well pull this off. 3: As this does not involve actually coming into contact with the man it has a fair chance of succeeding.

SCORES 1: 10 points. 2: 30 points. 3: 20 points.

b) 1-3:

1: You could never have that much strength in reserve. 2: A wise choice. 3: He probably wouldn't notice.

SCORES 1: 10 points. 2: 30 points. 3: 20 points.

c) 1-3:

1: Speed is the soundest course. 2: WARRIOR won't tire, though he *could* be taken unawares. 3: What's the matter? Tired of living?

    SCORES 1: 30 points. 2: 20 points. 3: 10 points.

d) 1-3:

1: Despite the lost seconds this could be the most sensible thing to do. 2: Courage and coolness could fend off his attack. 3: Some hope.

    SCORES 1: 30 points. 2: 20 points. 3: 10 points.

---

(4) JET

Her gymnastic and dance training makes JET particularly supple. She is an excellent sprinter.
As weight-training does not figure greatly in her regime this can put her at a slight disadvantage in events depending on strength.

Your best way of tackling this Gladiator is by forcing her into head-to-head confrontations rather than trying to out-pace her.

PRINCIPAL OPTION a)
Intermediate Options 1-3:

1: If there are enough seconds left, you could wear down JET. 2: The advantage is with her in a straight race. 3: Might work if you have enough of a head-start.

    SCORES 1: 30 points. 2: 10 points. 3: 20 points.

b) 1-3:

1: Fair chance of achieving this. 2: JET would certainly win. 3: Odds on pulling this off are fifty-fifty.

    SCORES 1: 30 points. 2: 10 points. 3: 20 points.

c) 1-3:

1: You could break away, but might not fare so well in the dash. 2: JET will stay alert and watchful. 3: Fortune favours you with this plan.

SCORES 1: 20 points. 2: 10 points. 3: 30 points.

d) 1-3:

1: Your lost seconds and JET's speed capabilities make this a poor choice. 2: A reasonable chance of success. 3: The best plan.

SCORES: 1: 10 points. 2: 20 points. 3: 30 points.

---

(5) SARACEN

Another Gladiator who is more likely to score well in encounters that call for strength. SARACEN also goes in for a lot of gym circuit work and athletics, however, and can summon surprising reserves of speed.

If possible, it is probably best to avoid having to face SARACEN when power is a crucial factor. The preferable strategy is to try to out-pace him.

PRINCIPAL OPTION a)
Intermediate Options 1-3:

1: You stand little chance of smashing SARACEN into submission in the time available. 2: Probably the most sensible thing to do. 3: This ploy could work if you don't linger.

SCORES 1: 10 points. 2: 30 points 3: 20 points.

b) 1-3:

1: The result of this course of action is finely balanced. 2: The best option. 3: SARACEN is a walking shock-absorber.

SCORES 1: 20 points. 2: 30 points. 3: 10 points.

c) 1-3:

1: Your best chance of emerging triumphant. 2: SARACEN will not wear down, but could be caught unawares. 3: You have to come off second best.

   SCORES 1: 30 points. 2: 20 points. 3: 10 points.

d) 1-3:

1: Providing you don't take too long regaining control this offers you your best chance. 2: The odds are on SARACEN this time. 3: Risky, but just possible.

   SCORES 1: 30 points. 2: 10 points. 3: 20 points.

---

(6) PHOENIX

Athleticism is the asset she uses to best effect, as demonstrated by her expertise in Thai and kick boxing. PHOENIX is the lightest of the women Gladiators, but still has the kind of strength you would expect from someone who works hard at developing muscle strength and tone.

   You would be most likely to fare well against her in power confrontations, less so where speed is called for.

PRINCIPAL OPTION a)
Intermediate Options 1-3:

1: If too much time hasn't gone by, this could work. 2: She would almost certainly get there before you. 3: Victory depends on how unexpectedly you change course.

   SCORES 1: 30 points. 2: 10 points. 3: 20 points.

b) 1-3:

1: If you have not already expended too much strength, this is a winning plan. 2: PHOENIX is better equipped to beat you at this. 3: Not impossible – this could work in your favour.

SCORES 1: 30 points. 2: 10 points. 3: 20 points.

c) 1-3:

1: Possible to break away, but you might not do so well in the race that follows. 2: She is tenacious, but you could outwit PHOENIX this way. 3: Gambling on this option could well pay off.

SCORES 1: 10 points. 2: 20 points. 3: 30 points.

d) 1-3:

1: You would have to regain control instantly for this to work. 2: With determination you should be able to fend off PHOENIX's assault. 3: She is likely to roll rings around you.

SCORES 1: 20 points. 2: 30 points. 3: 10 points.

---

(7) HAWK

Both strong and agile in roughly equal measures, HAWK is nevertheless more likely to shine when it comes to strength rather than fleet-footedness. But he does concentrate on overall fitness and can surprise contenders by pulling out all the stops and showing a clean pair of heels. HAWK is noted for his endurance and tenacity.

PRINCIPAL OPTION a)
Intermediate Options 1-3:

1: HAWK almost certainly has too much strength in reserve for this to be achieved. 2: He's fast, but this is your best bet. 3: A fair possibility if you are cunning enough about it.

SCORES 1: 10 points. 2: 30 points. 3: 20 points.

b) 1-3:

1: Get up a good head of speed and you might manage this.
2: Yes, better to try out-running than out-powering him.
3: It would take some crashing to disorientate HAWK.

SCORES 1: 20 points. 2: 30 points. 3: 10 points.

c) 1-3:

1: Assuming you put everything you have into this it looks like a good plan. 2: Maybe, but just as likely you would be rolling around forever. 3: HAWK certainly has the advantage with this option.

SCORES 1: 30 points. 2: 20 points. 3: 10 points.

d) 1-3:

1: Don't dally and you could come out a winner. 2: HAWK's attacks can be terminally ferocious. 3: A possibility of success if you dedicate yourself to the plan.

SCORES 1: 30 points. 2: 10 points. 3: 20 points.

---

(8) PANTHER

PANTHER is exceptionally good at Atlaspheres. Her sound all-round body tone and strength, and a regime that includes attention to both flexibility and power, make her a formidable opponent.

PANTHER is perhaps best confronted with force rather than a contest of speed.

PRINCIPAL OPTION a)
Intermediate Options 1-3:

1: PANTHER is resilient, but enough of a battering could do the trick. 2: Only good if you can get there first, which is by no means a foregone conclusion. 3: Atlaspheres is her best event and she is wise to these sort of tricks.

SCORES 1: 30 points. 2: 20 points. 3: 10 points.

b) 1-3:

1: This direct approach will probably prove best. 2: She'll be waiting for you. 3: With luck, yes; but don't put your shirt on it.

SCORES 1: 30 points. 2: 10 points. 3: 20 points.

c) 1-3:

1: PANTHER'S Atlaspheres expertise makes it unlikely she will fall for this. 2: You have the fairest chance with this cunning ploy. 3: Perhaps, providing she doesn't keep you at bay until time runs out.

SCORES 1: 10 points. 2: 30 points. 3: 20 points.

d) 1-3:

1: It won't wash with this Atlaspheres champion. 2: A reasonable option if you batten down the hatches. 3: Go for it.

SCORES 1: 10 points. 2: 20 points. 3: 30 points.

---

(9) WOLF

Compared to most of the male Gladiators, WOLF is a light-weight, clocking in at only fifteen stone. He makes up for this with his height, reach and strategic approach to the events. He weight-trains and does aerobics, as well as kick-boxing, so he qualifies as a good all-rounder.

WOLF is cunning and extrovert, so he is inclined to make bold and audacious moves when competing. Given the right set of circumstances he often, but not always, wins, when faced with a trial of strength.

PRINCIPAL OPTION a)
Intermediate Options 1-3:

1: Keep up your attack and you could be heading for a win. 2: WOLF is too smooth a mover to be bowled over by this. 3: Stranger things have happened.

SCORES 1: 30 points. 2: 10 points. 3: 20 points.

b) 1-3:

1: This sort of move can serve you best. 2: WOLF's agility militates against this. 3: With enough power this might work.

SCORES 1: 30 points. 2: 10 points. 3: 20 points.

c) 1-3:

1: A sharp turn of speed and no warning could bring this off. 2: If you act decisively when the moment comes this can be to your advantage. 3: He is too canny to let you connect with effect.

SCORES 1: 20 points. 2: 30 points. 3: 10 points.

d) 1-3:

1: A bad option with fleet WOLF. 2: Buckle down and you might get through the ordeal. 3: A direct approach like this offers your best chance.

SCORES 1: 10 points. 2: 20 points. 3: 30 points.

---

 (10) FLAME

Aerobic workouts, dancing and jogging indicate that FLAME's best assets are agility and speed. Her six foot frame means she has excellent reach.

Forcing her into endurance or power contests is more likely to pay off than trying to out-pace her.

PRINCIPAL OPTION a)
Intermediate Options 1-3:

1: Assuming you can pin her down, your battering stands a good chance of doing the trick. 2: FLAME will probably out-pace you. 3: Applied with subtlety this option has a possibility of succeeding.

SCORES 1: 30 points. 2: 10 points. 3: 20 points.

b) 1-3:

1: If you can summon up enough of a push this may work.
2: Her athletic training is to your disadvantage. 3: Sufficient energy behind your attack may bring this off.

SCORES 1: 20 points. 2: 10 points. 3: 30 points.

c) 1-3:

1: Delay can scupper this strategy. 2: The stakes are too high to rely on this working out. 3: A dedicated onslaught will see you gaining the points.

SCORES 1: 20 points. 2: 10 points. 3: 30 points.

d) 1-3:

1: FLAME's ability to move around the playing area with panache makes this the option least likely to succeed. 2: Decisively repelling her attack and a swift rush to a pod can ensure triumph. 3: Danger is in FLAME delaying you until the time is up.

SCORES 1: 10 points. 2: 30 points. 3: 20 points.

---

(11) COBRA

COBRA has remarkable bodily flexibility. Competitive body building has endowed him with strength, but agility is perhaps is greatest asset. He is probably best confronted with plans that require a strength-led response.

PRINCIPAL OPTION a)
Intermediate Options 1-3:

1: A battering could keep him off. 2: Your slithery opponent won't let this happen. 3: Perhaps, but COBRA's fluid movement could as easily thwart you.

SCORES 1: 30 points. 2: 10 points. 3: 20 points.

b) 1-3:

1: Iffy, as it depends on you having enough energy left.
2: You'll be following him. 3: A potential win if you strike
with as much force as possible.

SCORES 1: 20 points. 2: 10 points. 3: 30 points.

c) 1-3:

1: COBRA's mastery of the sphere makes breaking out
improbable. 2: Tiring him is remotely possible, pulling
the wool over his eyes more likely. 3: It will take some
doing, and an element of surprise, but this can be the best
approach.

SCORES 1: 10 points. 2: 20 points. 3: 30 points.

d) 1-3:

1: No matter how quickly you get control back, COBRA
will almost certainly out-run you. 2: Brace yourself and it
could happen. 3: Not easy, but it can be done.

SCORES 1: 10 points. 2: 30 points. 3: 20 points.

---

(12) LIGHTNING

LIGHTNING is especially proficient at Atlaspheres, having a good balance of strength and
athleticism. Go for a trial of strength. Powerful as
she is, speed and agility have the edge in her approach. But
you should not entirely rely on this, as her opponents in
Atlaspheres have found to their disadvantage.

PRINCIPAL OPTION a)
Intermediate Options 1-3:

1: A frontal assault can pay dividends. 2: You will find it
practically impossible to out-run her. 3: Only if you catch
her completely by surprise.

SCORES 1: 30 points. 2: 10 points. 3: 20 points.

b) 1-3:

1: If you can really deliver impact you might get by her. 2: Countering this sort of move is what makes LIGHTNING so good at this event. 3: The most productive option available.

SCORES 1: 20 points. 2: 10 points. 3: 30 points.

c) 1-3:

1: Maybe, but she can counter this kind of ploy. 2: She is too good at Atlaspheres to stand for this. 3: Yes, if you put every ounce of strength into it.

SCORES 1: 20 points. 2: 10 points. 3: 30 points.

d) 1-3:

1: LIGHTNING will sweep this plan aside. 2: Anchor down and you might come out in one piece. 3: Smash on through.

SCORES 1: 10 points. 2: 20 points. 3: 30 points.

(2) THE WALL

In this event the aim is to scale a towering thirty-six foot high wall. There are hand and footholds and you have sixty seconds to reach the top.

Ten seconds after you set off on the ascent, your Gladiator opponent starts out, determined to pull you off the wall, block your path or otherwise prevent you from reaching safety.

You score five points if you are still clinging to the wall when the sixty seconds are up. If you manage to shake off your opponent and get both legs over the top you score ten points.

PRINCIPAL OPTIONS

Pick one of the following ways of scaling The Wall.

Do you:

a) *Choose a complicated route up The Wall, relying on your ten second lead to leave the pursuing Gladiator with a tough job catching you?*

b) *Take the most direct route up The Wall in the hope that your athleticism will allow you to out-pace your opponent?*

c) *Pace yourself on your upward climb, making steady progress to the top, and relying on your agility to avoid the grasping hands of the Gladiator?*

d) *Power your way up the most convenient route, hoping that your strength will be great enough to shake off the best efforts of your opponent?*

INTERMEDIATE OPTIONS

Now choose one of the following **Intermediate Options**.

Remember to select it from the group corresponding to the **Principal Option** you went with.

P.O. a) What happens:

The complicated route you have chosen proves much more exhausting than you thought it would. Your stamina, and time, are both running out.

In response, you:

1. Abandon the idea of a convoluted route and go all-out for the top the most direct way possible.

2. Concentrate on securing good foot and hand-holds, anchor yourself as firmly as possible, and prepare to beat off your opponent.

3. Attempt to throw the Gladiator off your scent by adopting a seemingly erratic route.

P.O. b) What happens:

The Gladiator chasing you looks to be your equal in speed and agility.

In response, you:

1. Accept they will catch up with you and prepare to pit your strength against theirs in an all-out bid to dislodge them.

2. Plumb the depths of your energy resources to find a decisive burst of speed.

3. Attempt to throw the Gladiator off your scent by adopting a seemingly erratic route.

P.O. c) What happens:

You find that your opponent has out-flanked you and positioned himself above you on The Wall, blocking your upward path.

In response, you:

1. Move to one side and adopt a curving route that takes you well away and around the Gladiator.

2. Grab one of the Gladiator's ankles and try to pull them from The Wall.

3. Do your best to battle your way past them then put on as much speed as you can in a straight race to the top.

P.O. d) What happens:

About half-way up The Wall your Gladiator reaches you and manages to grasp your legs with his hand.

In response, you:

1. Stay with your plan and put all you have into shaking your opponent off so you can resume your ascent.

2. Go all the way and not only shake off your opponent but do your best to send him/her plunging to the floor below.

3. Put aside the idea of matching your strength with your opponent, squirm out of his/her grasp, and put on all speed for a direct scramble to victory.

Event Two
THE WALL
SCORE CHECK

The Gladiators' biographies (page 5), and the notes about them in the Atlaspheres Score Check (page 14), will give you everything you need to know about their abilities. From here on you will only be reminded of which events the Gladiators are best at. In this section, that means SCORPIO, JET, SARACEN and PHOENIX.

(1) SHADOW

PRINCIPAL OPTION a)
Intermediate options 1-3:

1: The option best designed to succeed. 2: You would be eating the floor. 3: This probably increases SHADOW's chances of winning.

SCORES 1: 30 points. 2: 10 points. 3: 20 points.

b) 1-3:

1: Say hello to the ground. 2: A good decision. 3: This might work if you can combine a zig-zag path with speed.

SCORES 1: 10 points. 2: 30 points. 3: 20 points.

c) 1-3:

1: Fine, providing you can avoid SHADOW's grasp. 2: The least likely to succeed. 3: The speed part is OK, the battling past bit more of a problem.

SCORES 1: 30 points. 2: 10 points. 3: 20 points.

d) 1-3:

1: It can be done, with great difficulty. 2: Chances are you are the one about to get acquainted with the floor. 3: How very sensible.

SCORES 1: 20 points. 2: 10 points. 3: 30 points.

---

(2) SCORPIO

The wall is her best event.

PRINCIPAL OPTION a)
Intermediate Options 1-3:

1: SCORPIO could well be there when you arrive. 2: A good way of stopping her in her tracks. 3: You would need a good quota of luck and extra stamina.

SCORES 1: 10 points. 2: 30 points. 3: 20 points.

b) 1-3:

1: Victory can be yours. 2: SCORPIO usually moves faster. 3: This has its merits but may not take her swiftness sufficiently into account.

SCORES 1: 30 points. 2: 10 points. 3: 20 points.

c) 1-3:

1: Could be, but SCORPIO's a pretty good out-flanker herself. 2: A good tug could bring in the points. 3: You may well be able to fight past, the race is another story.

SCORES 1: 20 points 2: 30 points. 3: 10 points.

d) 1-3:

1: Shaking off this opponent is possible, but she'll be after you again. 2: You can do it. 3: A mistake; you should have gone for strength, not speed.

SCORES 1: 20 points. 2: 30 points. 3: 10 points.

---

(3) WARRIOR
PRINCIPAL OPTION a)
Intermediate Options 1-3:

1: Go hell for leather and watch those points clock up. 2: He's going to peel you off, isn't he? 3: Your stamina is likely to give out before WARRIOR's, so it depends on how much confusion you can sow.

SCORES 1: 30 points. 2: 10 points. 3: 20 points.

b) 1-3:

1: Say hi to everybody in the casualty department. 2: A fine plan. 3: There's something to be said for this, providing WARRIOR doesn't get within clutching distance.

SCORES 1: 10 points. 2: 30 points. 3: 20 points.

c) 1-3:

1: Avoidance is a good strategy in these circumstances. 2: Get *real*. 3: Sure, if you can survive the battle to pass him.

SCORES 1: 30 points. 2: 10 points. 3: 20 points.

d) 1-3:

1: You might get away with it. 2: You almost certainly won't get away with it. 3: It will take some serious squirming, but speed is the decisive factor.

SCORES 1: 20 points. 2: 10 points, 3: 30 points.

---

(4) JET
The Wall is one of JET's best events

PRINCIPAL OPTION 1)
Intermediate Options 1-3:

1: The money is on JET being ahead of you. 2: You'll take a buffeting, but it's a good plan. 3: Maybe this will pan out, maybe not.

SCORES 1: 10 points. 2: 30 points. 3: 20 points.

b) 1-3:

It's going to be a hard, close fight, but your perseverance could win the day. 2: She's seen this one before. 3: This one is not unknown to JET, but there's an outside chance of it working.

SCORES 1: 30 points. 2: 10 points. 3: 20 points.

c) 1-3:

1: JET has a good line in cutting-off contenders taking con-

32

voluted routes. 2: Providing you put in the effort you may have the satisfaction of waving as she falls past you. 3: Battling past: yes; race to the top: not as certain.

SCORES 1: 10 points. 2: 30 points. 3: 20 points.

d) 1-3:

1: You could shake her off, only to find her on your back again. 2: Bye-bye JET. 3: Not recommended, all things considered.

SCORES 1: 20 points. 2: 30 points. 3: 10 points.

---

(5) SARACEN

The Wall is one of SARACEN's best events.

PRINCIPAL OPTION a)
Intermediate Options 1-3:

1: If you call pull out all the stops, a direct scramble looks promising. 2: SARACEN is not to be beaten so easily. 3: Only a fair chance.

SCORES 1: 30 points. 2: 10 points. 3: 20 points.

b) 1-3:

1: Little chance of dislodging this Gladiator. 2: Yes, if you go like a rocket. 3: A possibility.

SCORES 1: 10 points. 2: 30 points. 3: 20 points.

c) 1-3:

1: With guile and speed you could manage this. 2: A big enough pull *might* dislodge him. 3: Best not try it.

SCORES 1: 30 points. 2: 20 points. 3: 10 points.

d) 1-3:

1: If you can shake like an earthquake. 2: More likely *you* will crush the carpet. 3: Don't hesitate and it can happen.

SCORES 1: 20 points. 2: 10 points. 3: 30 points.

---

(6) PHOENIX

The wall is one of PHOENIX's best events.

PRINCIPAL OPTION a)
Intermediate Options 1-3:

1: Only a good plan if your speed is greater than agile PHOENIX's. 2: You may have found her Achilles' heel. 3: Unlikely to impress this champion of The Wall.

SCORES 1: 20 points. 2: 30 points. 3: 10 points.

b) 1-3:

1: Be tenacious and you could emerge the winner. 2: You are playing into her hands. 3: A slim chance.

SCORES 1: 30 points. 2: 10 points. 3: 20 points.

c) 1-3:

1: Do this and PHOENIX will demonstrate why she excels on The Wall. 2: Yes, if you give it all you've got. 3: Only a good battering will slow her pursuit.

SCORES 1: 10 points. 2: 30 points. 3: 20 points.

d) 1-3:

1: She will take some shaking. 2: An unrelenting attack will serve you well. 3: No; strength is a better option than playing PHOENIX at her own game.

SCORES 1: 20 points. 2: 30 points. 3: 10 points.

(7) HAWK
PRINCIPAL OPTION a)
Intermediate Options 1-3:

1: A decisive burst of speed can leave him stranded. 2: Good chance he'll strip you off like Wall paper. 3: All right if you can ration your stamina.

SCORES 1: 30 points. 2: 10 points. 3: 20 points.

b) 1-3:

1: Super-fit HAWK may well make mincemeat of you. 2: A single-minded upward spurt can leave your opponent behind. 3: Perhaps, but you run the risk of tiring out first.

SCORES 1: 10 points. 2: 30 points. 3: 20 points.

c) 1-3:

1: This avoids tangling with HAWK, so is advisable. 2: It takes a lot to beat him off. 3: Something to be said for this, but it's a gamble.

SCORES 1: 30 points. 2: 10 points. 3: 20 points.

d) 1-3:

1: Getting away could be a problem. 2: Learn to fly, fast. 3: Don't look back and keep your eye on the top.

SCORES 1: 20 points. 2: 10 points. 3: 30 points.

---

(8) PANTHER
PRINCIPAL OPTION a)
Intermediate Options 1-3:

1: Her light weight and muscular frame make her the favourite in this option. 2: PANTHER can be forced off. 3: You could be handing it to her on a plate.

SCORES 1: 10 points. 2: 30 points. 3: 20 points.

b) 1-3:

1: It will involve a good scrap, but this can be made to work. 2: PANTHER is an out-pacing paragon. 3: She can anticipate this sort of thing unless you are exceptionally cunning.

SCORES 1: 30 points. 2: 10 points. 3: 20 points.

c) 1-3:

1: PANTHER can deal with this without raising sweat. 2: Make like a bell-ringer and watch her sail past. 3: Assuming you get away, she could be right after you.

SCORES 1: 10 points. 2: 30 points. 3: 20 points.

d) 1-3:

1: She will be back with you almost instantly. 2: A good pummelling can see her off. 3: Something to be said for this if you don't hang around.

SCORES 1: 10 points. 2: 30 points. 3: 20 points.

---

(9) WOLF
PRINCIPAL OPTION a)
Intermediate Options 1-3:

1: Athletic WOLF would certainly out-pace you. 2: Hang on tight, fight for dear life, and you have an excellent chance. 3: Maybe, but your failing energy and WOLF's agility are a bad mix.

SCORES 1: 10 points. 2: 30 points. 3: 20 points.

b) 1-3:

1: Face him head-on for the best chance of a win. 2: WOLF will likely match you. 3: This is possible, if doubtful, because it uses up precious energy.

SCORES 1: 30 points. 2: 10 points 3: 20 points.

c) 1-3:

1: It means keeping your cool and taking WOLF off-guard. 2: He can be levered away. 3: You could still be fighting for right of way when the whistle goes.

SCORES 1: 20 points. 2: 30 points. 3: 10 points.

d) 1-3:

1: Your determination and speed could prove the deciding factors. 2: Could be a long battle. 3: Speed-dashes are his province.

SCORES 1: 30 points. 2: 20 points. 3: 10 points.

---

(10) FLAME
PRINCIPAL OPTION a)
Intermediate Options 1-3:

1: You have used valuable energy and you're up against a nifty mover, so no to this. 2: She is one of the biggest female Gladiators but if you stay in there you can down her. 3: Maybe, but she has the advantage.

SCORES 1: 10 points. 2: 30 points. 3: 20 points.

b) 1-3:

1: Grasp those holds and tear into her. 2: FLAME's speed is probably better. 3: Possibly a good option if you can match her speed and athleticism.

SCORES 1: 30 points. 2: 10 points. 3: 20 points.

c) 1-3:

1: FLAME's all-round fitness has the edge on you in this sort of plan. 2: Keep away from those long legs, cling like a limpet, and your chances are good. 3: Depends on how far you get before she's after you.

SCORES 1: 10 points. 2: 30 points. 3: 20 points.

d) 1-3:

1: First part of plan: very possible; second part of plan: probably not. 2: Apply your weight to bringing her down. 3: She has all the qualities needed to stop you doing this.

SCORES 1: 20 points. 2: 30 points. 3: 10 points.

---

(11) COBRA
PRINCIPAL OPTION a)
Intermediate Options 1-3:

1: COBRA will slither on past you. 2: Too close to call this one. 3: A bulls-eye if your energy holds out.

SCORES 1: 10 points. 2: 20 points. 3: 30 points.

b) 1-3:

1: Deliver an unmerciful onslaught and COBRA could go down. 2: COBRA's speed is formidable. 3: His agility could tell if you are unlucky.

SCORES 1: 30 points. 2: 10 points. 3: 20 points.

c) 1-3

1: Chance is he'll anticipate this one. 2: A tough job but by no means an impossible one. 3: He's an all-rounder; you could fail at either stage.

SCORES 1: 10 points. 2: 30 points. 3: 20 points.

d) 1-3:

1: A doubtful option that must take COBRA's agility into account. 2: A good tug and COBRA could be taking flying lessons. 3: The victory is more likely to be his in a straight race.

SCORES 1: 20 points. 2: 30 points. 3: 10 points.

---

(12) **LIGHTNING**
PRINCIPAL OPTION a)
Intermediate Options 1-3:

1: LIGHTNING has energy to spare; by now you don't. 2: It's no tea party, but you can achieve this. 3: Only if you can access more stamina.

SCORES 1: 10 points. 2: 30 points. 3: 20 points.

b) 1-3:

1: It will hurt at the time but you'll be glad you did this. 2: Decisive bursts of speed are LIGHTNING's department. 3: It may not prove erratic enough to lose her.

SCORES 1: 30 points. 2: 10 points. 3: 20 points.

c) 1-3:

1: LIGHTNING will streak on over to you. 2: This can bring her down in a flash. 3: Perhaps, but she can flash back into action pretty fast.

SCORES 1: 10 points. 2: 30 points. 3: 20 points.

d) 1-3:

1: One shake and she's back. 2: A stormy but ultimately worthwhile option. 3: You may not be able to squirm away from greased LIGHTNING.

SCORES 1: 10 points. 2: 30 points. 3: 20 points.

(3) DANGER ZONE

There are four safety stations placed around the playing area. Behind each is a different kind of projectile weapon, such as a crossbow, mortar or rocket-launcher. You have one minute to run to each of the stations in sequence to secure the weapon.

You are being watched by your Gladiator, standing on a platform at one end of the arena, who has a target mounted above him. You have to try and hit this target with each of the weapons you find in the safety stations.

Your Gladiator opponent is armed with a tennis ball launcher that pumps out its ammo at a speed of one hundred miles an hour – in your direction! If one of these balls hits you, you're out of the game.

As an added refinement the safety stations are timed to auto-destruct at successive ten second intervals unless you defuse them.

If you get to the fourth station without having hit the target above the Gladiator's head, you must climb through a perspex cylinder which has holes in the top to allow your opponent's tennis balls through. Assuming you manage this, and arrive at the vantage point beyond, you then aim for a target below the Gladiator.

The score is one point for every weapon you are able to fire. That becomes a total score of ten points if you hit the target.

Danger Zone is a ballistic battle requiring speed, the ability to dodge, and dead-eye aiming on the part of the contender.

PRINCIPAL OPTIONS

Do you:

a) *Concentrate all your efforts on hitting the target mounted above your Gladiator foe's head in order to score maximum points?*

b) *Direct your efforts to reaching and firing as many of the weapons as possible in order to accumulate points that way?*

c) *Make dodging the tennis balls your opponent is pumping at you your first priority, to avoid disqualification?*

d) *Do all you can to defuse the four safety stations before they auto-destruct and deprive you of the weapons?*

INTERMEDIATE OPTIONS

P.O. a) What happens:

Hitting the target proves a much harder task than you thought.

In response, you:

1. Persevere with your efforts to hit the target in the expectation that your aim will improve as each shot gives you a better bead on it.

2. Abandon the idea of hitting the target, concentrating instead on reaching and firing as many of the weapons as possible.

3. Resign yourself to not being able to hit the target from any of the safety stations and hope you can make it through the perspex tube for a crack at the target below the Gladiator.

P.O. b) What happens:

The stream of tennis balls directed at you by your Gladiator enemy is so unrelenting you constantly find yourself pinned down.

In response, you:

1: Change tack and direct your efforts to hitting the target.

2. Carry on regardless, trusting in your speed and agility to help you avoid being hit.

3. Zig-zag your way from one station to the next in an attempt to spoil the Gladiator's aim.

P.O. c) What happens:

The Gladiator has a much better aim than you expected, and you come dangerously close to being hit by a ball and finding yourself out of the game.

In response, you:

1. Scurry across the playing floor low and fast to make yourself as hard a target to hit as possible.

2. Get to each station as quickly as you can, then direct a constant spray of ammo towards the target in the hope that at least one will get through.

3. Go for a station with the intention of firing just a few shots at the target but making each one count by spending as long as you dare taking careful aim.

P.O. d) What happens:

You underestimated how long this option will take you to perform and time is running out.

In response, you:

1. Switch to trying to hit the target instead.

2. Reach for greater speed in a bid to better your progress time from station to station.

3. Centre your efforts on getting to the weapons and firing them to build up points.

Event Three
DANGER ZONE
SCORE CHECK

(1) SHADOW
PRINCIPAL OPTION a)
Intermediate Options 1-3:

1: Your aim is unlikely to improve in the time available. 2: You accumulate maximum points this way. 3: SHADOW scores a hit against you as you scramble up the tube.

SCORES 1: 20 points. 2: 30 points. 3: 10 points.

b) 1-3:

1: You have a better than good chance of hitting the target providing you stay cool. 2: Dangerous because it tempts fate and you could easily be hit. 3: An OK option but bear in mind that SHADOW is firing off his ammo like a hosepipe.

SCORES 1: 30 points. 2: 10 points. 3: 20 points.

c) 1-3:

1: This improves your chances of survival somewhat. 2: A constant stream of fire increases the odds in favour of a hit. 3: Too time-consuming.

SCORES 1: 20 points. 2: 30 points. 3: 10 points.

d) 1-3:

1: Too problematic as time, and SHADOW's sharp eye, are against you. 2: As you have presumably been going at top speed anyway there may be nothing in reserve. 3: Going for quantity rather than quality points this way could be best.

SCORES 1: 10 points. 2: 20 points. 3: 30 points.

(2) SCORPIO
PRINCIPAL OPTION a)
Intermediate Options 1-3:

1: This leaves you too open to SCORPIO's bombardment.
2: A risk because it means over-exposing yourself to enemy
fire. 3: This last-ditch option could bring an accolade.

SCORES 1: 10 points. 2: 20 points 3: 30 points.

b) 1-3:

1: Plump for this option and with a calm approach you
could score. 2: Poor choice as you make yourself a hostage
to fortune. 3: You just might throw off SCORPIO's aim
this way.

SCORES 1: 30 points. 2: 10 points. 3: 20 points.

c) 1-3:

1: Not too likely to put off the tenacious SCORPIO. 2:
Piling on the shots brings victory within your grasp. 3:
You lost too much time dodging all those balls earlier.

SCORES 1: 20 points. 2: 30 points. 3: 10 points.

d) 1-3:

1: A bit late in the day to take up this option. 2: You have
SCORPIO's cross-fire to negotiate. 3: At least this means
racking up some points.

SCORES 1: 10 points. 2: 20 points. 3: 30 points.

(3) WARRIOR
PRINCIPAL OPTION a)
Intermediate Options 1-3:

1: This could work against WARRIOR, gambling on his reaction time being slightly slower than yours. 2: Time could work against you by switching options at this point. 3: The nearer to WARRIOR the less likely you are to avoid his shots.

SCORES 1: 30 points. 2: 20 points. 3: 10 points.

b) 1-3:

1: The shower of projectiles raining down on you makes accurate aiming a nightmare. 2: You might dodge WARRIOR's shots but don't underestimate his capacity to keep them coming. 3: An erratic course is the best way of dealing with the situation.

SCORES 1: 10 points. 2: 20 points. 3: 30 points.

c) 1-3:

1: You can out-pace WARRIOR's volley. 2: Not a bad idea if you have enough seconds in hand. 3: A real long-shot.

SCORES 1: 30 points. 2: 20 points. 3: 10 points.

d) 1-3:

1: Not enough time left for thoughtful shots. 2: This would be good if you have the reserve speed. 3: You have a ballistic downpour to avoid between stations, so get a move on.

SCORES 1: 10 points. 2: 30 points. 3: 20 points.

---

(4) JET
PRINCIPAL OPTION a)
Intermediate Options 1-3:

1: Why flog a dead horse? 2: Not a bad alternative, but you have to run JET's gauntlet. 3: A council of desperation perhaps, but it offers the chance of scoring.

SCORES 1: 10 points. 2: 20 points. 3: 30 points.

b) 1-3:

1: The best choice in the sense that you now have little alternative. 2: You offer too easy a target. 3: This makes you more difficult to hit but you are still exposed.

SCORES 1: 30 points. 2: 10 points. 3: 20 points.

c) 1-3:

1: JET will keep up her barrage, increasing her chances of a hit every time. 2: Constantly spraying the target area has its advantages. 3: Match your careful aim against JET's and you gamble wisely.

SCORES 1: 10 points. 2: 20 points. 3: 30 points.

d) 1-3:

1: This may mean burning up the few seconds of playing time you have left with possibly no result. 2: You still have to avoid JET's fusillade. 3: Ringing up the points like this is a smart option.

SCORES 1: 10 points. 2: 20 points. 3: 30 points.

---

(5) SARACEN
PRINCIPAL OPTION a)
Intermediate Options 1-3:

1: If at first you don't succeed... 2: This means abandoning the time you have invested in getting a bead on the target. 3: A problematic fall-back choice.

SCORES 1: 30 points. 2: 10 points. 3: 20 points.

b) 1-3:

1: Fate could favour you if one of SARACEN's tennis balls doesn't. 2: Unless you like being a sitting duck. 3: Difficult seeing as how SARACEN is more spraying than directing shots at you.

SCORES 1: 30 points. 2: 10 points. 3: 20 points.

c) 1-3:

1: Assuming SARACEN's aim isn't going to get worse, this could be a bit dumb. 2: There is some merit in pumping out the ordnance. 3: Make them all count, contender.

SCORES 1: 10 points. 2: 20 points 3: 30 points.

d) 1-3:

1: Why change horse mid-stream? 2: A change of plan now means you will throw away any progress gained. 3: Rapid fire could bring in some points.

SCORES 1: 10 points. 2: 20 points. 3: 30 points.

---

(6) PHOENIX
PRINCIPAL OPTION a)
Intermediate Options 1-3:

1: This is a reasonable expectation; stick with it. 2: Not a bad alternative if you're doing so poorly. 3: Your chances of getting this far are remote.

SCORES 1: 30 points. 2: 20 points. 3: 10 points.

b) 1-3:

1: Cutting your losses and trying this option could be fruit-ful. 2: Given PHOENIX's litheness, you run the risk of her moving to a better firing position against you. 3: Maybe this will work, but don't bet your life on it.

SCORES 1: 30 points. 2: 10 points. 3: 20 points.

c) 1-3:

1: You give PHOENIX the opportunity to bring you down. 2: An all-out response of this kind could bring you through. 3: With luck and nerves of steel, maybe.

SCORES 1: 10 points. 2: 30 points. 3: 20 points.

d) 1-3:

1: You admit you made a bad choice in the first place and try to redeem yourself. 2: If you have any speed left, this might serve you. 3: Pour out that ammo with a will.

SCORES 1: 10 points. 2: 20 points. 3: 30 points.

---

(7) HAWK
PRINCIPAL OPTION a)
Intermediate Options 1-3:

1: To some extent this involves exposing yourself to HAWK's fire and could be chancy. 2: Going for a quantity response has much in its favour. 3: The path to the tube is too fraught with peril to make it a certainty.

SCORES 1: 20 points. 2: 30 points. 3: 10 points.

b) 1-3:

1: Only if you can concentrate under fire. 2: This means risking HAWK-eye's deadly aim. 3: Bank on making yourself too hard to hit.

SCORES 1: 20 points. 2: 10 points. 3: 30 points.

c) 1-3:

1: Not much chance of dodging HAWK's missiles this way. 2: There is safety, and possibly points, in numbers. 3: Sometimes fate is kind.

SCORES 1: 10 points. 2: 30 points. 3: 20 points.

d) 1-3:

1: Why not undertake this potentially point-scoring venture? 2: If you haven't already given it all you've got, forget it. 3: You work on the assumption that HAWK won't

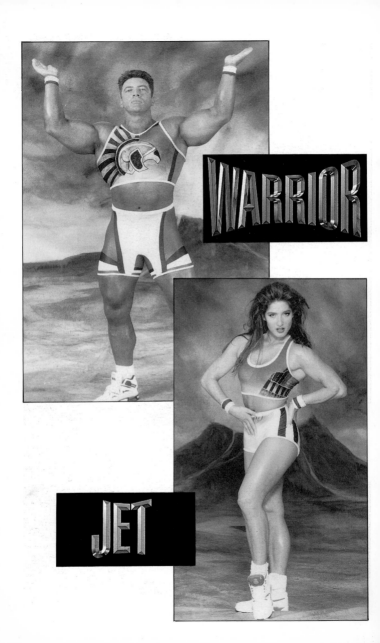

WARRIOR

JET

TM (c) LWT Programmes Ltd. 1992

WOLF

FLAME

cut you down on the way.

SCORES 1: 30 points. 2: 10 points. 3: 20 points.

---

(8) PANTHER
PRINCIPAL OPTION
Intermediate Options 1-3:

1: There is an argument for carrying on and hoping to attract luck. 2: PANTHER is not going to make it easy for you to reach the stations. 3: As a flanking move this can be most effective.

SCORES 1: 20 points. 2: 10 points. 3: 30 points.

b) 1-3:

1: Trying to salvage the situation this way is a mature decision that may pay off. 2: No, because athletic PANTHER can move fast enough to get off a tennis ball with your name on it. 3: An improvement, but you still invite PANTHER's volley.

SCORES 1: 30 points. 2: 10 points. 3: 20 points.

c) 1-3:

1: Zigging, zagging, dodging and rolling can fend off PANTHER's attack 2: Haphazard, but sometimes effective. 3: Time has been wasted.

SCORES 1: 30 points. 2: 20 points. 3: 10 points.

d) 1-3:

1: A careful aim and cool head can rescue you. 2: *If* you have the energy left, do it. 3: An unwise change of tack at this late stage.

SCORES 1: 30 points. 2: 20 points. 3: 10 points.

---

(9) WOLF
PRINCIPAL OPTION a)
Intermediate Options 1-3:

1: Don't give up now and you could be triumphant. 2: A fifty-fifty option. 3: Wily WOLF probably won't let you get this far.

SCORES 1: 30 points. 2: 20 points 3: 10 points.

b) 1-3:

1: This won't stop WOLF showering projectiles down on you. 2: Spoiling WOLF's aim is a sound bet. 3: Your cool opponent could anticipate your moves too well for comfort.

SCORES 1: 10 points. 2: 30 points. 3: 20 points.

c) 1-3:

1: Cunning WOLF's quick reflexes won't allow this. 2: WOLF would find it hard to counter this option. 3: If you are confident in your ability to zero in on the target, a canny move.

SCORES 1: 10 points. 2: 30 points. 3: 20 points.

d) 1-3:

1: Maybe you can snatch victory from the jaws of defeat this way. 2: With your depleted strength, and WOLF using you for target practice, not a good move. 3: Blaze away.

SCORES 1: 20 points. 2: 10 points. 3: 30 points.

---

(10) FLAME
PRINCIPAL OPTION a)
Intermediate Options 1-3:

1: If you thought this was a good idea to start with, keep on and be lucky. 2: A sound second line of defence if you can avoid getting hit in the process. 3: Even if you make the tube you have agile FLAME to contend with.

SCORES 1: 30 points. 2: 20 points. 3: 10 points.

b) 1-3:

1: This could be sufficiently confusing enough to your opponent that it will work. 2: FLAME will thank you for making yourself an easy target. 3: Some chance of success.

SCORES 1: 30 points. 2: 10 points. 3: 20 points.

c) 1-3:

1: FLAME should not have too much trouble picking you off. 2: Overwhelm her and the target with a torrent of fire. 3: Requires too much luck and more time than you probably have left.

SCORES 1: 10 points. 2: 30 points. 3: 20 points.

d) 1-3:

1: Too little too late. 2: Put your heart into a speed trial. 3: You could bring this off if there is time left to you.

SCORES 1: 10 points. 2: 30 points. 3: 20 points.

---

(11) COBRA
PRINCIPAL OPTION a)
Intermediate Options 1-3:

1: If your aim hasn't improved by now why force the issue? 2: This could put you back in the game with a winning chance. 3: A perilous if possibly good option.

SCORES 1: 10 points. 2: 30 points. 3: 20 points.

b) 1-3:

1: Only nerves of ice will improve your aim as the seconds tick by. 2: You take the chance of COBRA nailing you. 3: The prize is yours if you take this risk.

SCORES 1: 10 points. 2: 20 points. 3: 30 points.

c) 1-3:

1: If COBRA's aim is *that* good, no amount of ducking is going to help. 2: You're home and dry if just one ball gets through. 3: An outside chance of winning through.

SCORES 1: 10 points. 2: 30 points. 3: 20 points.

d) 1-3:

1: This may or may not rescue the situation, depending on how late in the event you do it. 2: You haven't used all your speed yet? 3: Build your points like this.

SCORES 1: 20 points. 2: 10 points 3: 30 points.

---

(12) LIGHTNING
PRINCIPAL OPTION a)
Intermediate Options 1-3:

1: Better try your luck at another option. 2: An all-out assault could get you across the winning line. 3: Dangerous but not impossible to undertake.

SCORES 1: 10 points. 2: 30 points. 3: 20 points.

b) 1-3:

1: As this involves a chance to confuse your opponent it could succeed. 2: This tempts another LIGHTNING strike. 3: The gods could be kind to you.

SCORES 1: 30 points. 2: 10 points. 3: 20 points.

c) 1-3:

1: Could make you a LIGHTNING conductor. 2: Indiscriminate firing might help you strike lucky. 3: Go in steady, ignoring LIGHTNING's onslaught, and one of your shots could count.

SCORES 1: 10 points. 2: 20 points. 3: 30 points.

d) 1-3:

1: You should have forgot it and gone on to another option. 2: LIGHTNING's bolts will pursue you, remember. 3: Sprinkle the target enough and the effect could be pleasing.

SCORES 1: 10 points. 2: 20 points. 3: 30 points.

★
(4) SWINGSHOT

In Swingshot you compete against the Gladiator while both of you are suspended on flexible shock-cords attached to the ceiling.

Your starting point is a fifteen foot high platform. In front of you is a pole divided into three colours. When you jump and hit the floor the shock cord will zap you back up into the air. The object at this stage is to grab a ball from a cylinder on one of the three coloured areas on the pole — yellow at twenty feet, blue at twenty-two feet or red at twenty-four feet.

Then you plunge back to the ground and bounce up again to your platform, where the ball is deposited in a basket. Yellow balls score one point, blue balls two points and red balls three points. You cannot attempt to retrieve any balls that may have fallen to the floor.

Swingshot would be hard enough without a Gladiator in your way. But of course one will be, using dexterity and might to stop you reaching the balls. This event calls for a high standard of both athleticism and timing. And don't overlook how dizzyingly disorientating all that zooming around will be.

PRINCIPAL OPTIONS

Do you:

a) *Decide to go only for red balls to increase your chance of higher scores?*

b) *Make only for the yellow ball level in order to conserve your strength and accumulate more points in the long run?*

c) *Use what you hope will be superior strength and agility to fight off your opponent's attacks?*

d)   *Endeavour to mislead the Gladiator by appearing to go for red balls but in fact ignoring them and grabbing one of the other colours on your way down?*

INTERMEDIATE OPTIONS

P.O. a) What happens:

The effort of reaching the twenty-four foot red ball level, and the battering assaults of your opponent, are rapidly tiring you.

In response, you:

1. Change your tactics and take any of the balls you are able to reach, no matter what their colour.

2. Only go for red balls every second or third leap, offering your opponent no regular pattern he or she can predict and foil.

3. Turn your energies towards taking on the Gladiator and go for one of the balls while they are still reeling from your onslaught.

P.O. b) What happens:

Going for the yellow balls means your Gladiator knows what you are about to do each time, which enables him/her to anticipate and block your jumps.

In response, you:

1. Make leaps of different heights at random, ensuring the pattern is broken.

2. Steel yourself to battle your opponent for possession of the balls.

3. Feign going for one particular colour of ball in an attempt to distract the Gladiator, then grab another.

P.O. c) What happens:

Your Gladiator rival seems at least your equal in strength and agility.

In response, you:

1. Battle on, convinced you must ultimately wear your opponent down.

2. Put more power into your leaps with the idea that the shock-cord will snap you ever higher and out of the reach of the Gladiator.

3. Go for more precise timing by holding back your jump until your opponent is too poorly positioned to reach you.

P.O. d) What happens:

This fails to work because the Gladiator does not care which coloured balls you are aiming for and simply swoops on you every time you are mid-leap.

In response, you

1. Tense yourself to slug it out, hoping that you can throw the Gladiator off-balance long enough to make a successful jump.

2. Pretend to be about to make a jump but hold yourself back at the last minute, counting on your adversary mistiming his/her own jump as a result.

3. Make a series of light jumps that barely takes you up to the lowest coloured area, then unexpectedly break this routine with one power-leap taking you to the highest level, looking to profit from the Gladiator's confusion at this.

Event Four
SWINGSHOT
SCORE CHECK

(1) SHADOW
PRINCIPAL OPTION a)
Intermediate Options 1-3:

1: As this will appear random to your opponent he will not be able to predict your next move. 2: This is itself a pattern and SHADOW won't take long realising it. 3: SHADOW is tough and you are tired; no more than an even chance of knocking him away.

SCORES 1: 30 points. 2: 10 points. 3: 20 points.

b) 1-3:

1: A satisfying confusing ploy that can have you racking up the points. 2: Super-fit SHADOW has to have the advantage. 3: SHADOW may well rumble this one.

SCORES 1: 30 points. 2: 10 points. 3: 20 points.

c) 1-3:

1: Try jumping over the moon while you're at it. 2: If you are sure of your agility, SHADOW could be foiled by this. 3: This relies on SHADOW allowing himself to be badly positioned in the first place which he might not be.

SCORES 1: 10 points. 2: 30 points. 3: 20 points.

d) 1-3:

1: Difficult to slug it out with SHADOW successfully. 2: Yes, but it could be a plan that only works once or twice. 3: There is a margin for success here but your timing has to be spot-on.

SCORES 1: 10 points. 1: 30 points. 3: 20 points.

---

(2) **SCORPIO**
PRINCIPAL OPTION a)
Intermediate Options 1-3:

1: SCORPIO will continue her stinging attacks regardless. 2: This may confuse your opponent but don't underestimate her ability to see through you. 3: Put everything into crashing her aside and you could be reaching for those points.

SCORES 1: 10 points. 2: 20 points. 3: 30 points.

b) 1-3:

1: Be cautious; no pattern is in itself a kind of pattern. 2: SCORPIO is strong but you can smash her away from your prizes. 3: She'll still come in for the kill.

SCORES 1: 20 points. 2: 30 points. 3: 10 points.

c) 1-3:

1: Providing you don't wear down yourself, this is an attractive option. 2: You may get higher but SCORPIO could catch you on the way back. 3: Her timing is at least as accurate as yours.

SCORES 1: 30 points. 2: 20 points. 3: 10 points.

d) 1-3:

1: A thorough battering can throw her off. 2: SCORPIO is too agile to let this occur. 3: Maybe, but her confusion may be short-lived.

SCORES 1: 30 points. 2: 10 points. 3: 20 points.

(3) WARRIOR
PRINCIPAL OPTION a)
Intermediate Options 1-3:

1: Taking what you can get makes sense. 2: A viable option if you can avoid your opponent's grasp. 3: Chances are you would be the one reeling.

   SCORES 1: 30 points. 2: 20 points. 3: 10 points.

b) 1-3:

1: Sowing confusion this way is a good weapon against most opponents. 2: A reckless choice. 3: This has its advocates.

   SCORES 1: 30 points. 2: 10 points. 3: 20 points.

c) 1-3:

1: It could take forever. 2: All right, but WARRIOR's great bulk means he could as easily reach dizzying heights too. 3: The leading option.

   SCORES 1: 10 points. 2: 20 points. 3: 30 points.

d) 1-3:

1: See you when you regain consciousness. 2: WARRIOR can be wrong-footed in these circumstances. 3: Perhaps you'll pull it off.

   SCORES 1: 10 points. 2: 20 points. 3: 30 points.

---

(4) JET
Swingshot is one of JET's best events.

PRINCIPAL OPTION a)
Intermediate Options 1-3:

1: A Swingshot expert, JET won't let this get by her. 2:

Might put her off for a while. 3: You could send her reel-ing.

SCORES 1: 10 points. 2: 20 points. 3: 30 points.

b) 1-3:

1: No. JET will see through this. 2: With determination you can gain possession. 3: Might work for a while.

SCORES 1: 10 points. 2: 30 points. 3: 20 points.

c) 1-3:

1: The battle will be bloody but you stand a good chance of winning it. 2: Could disorientate her. 3: JET knows how to put a stop to this sort of thing.

SCORES 1: 30 points. 2: 20 points. 3: 10 points.

d) 1-3:

1: A good body-slam can work wonders. 2: JET's agility will save her from this. 3: It *might* work in your favour.

SCORES 1: 30 points. 2: 10 points. 3: 20 points.

---

(5) SARACEN
PRINCIPAL OPTION a)
Intermediate Options 1-3:

1: Perhaps you can get away with this a couple of times. 2: An option definitely worth taking up. 3: Probably not cost-effective in terms of energy expended.

SCORES 1: 20 points. 2: 30 points. 3: 10 points.

b) 1-3:

1: A good ploy in this event. 2: The odds are in favour of SARACEN coming out on top. 3: Bound to work, but how many times?

SCORES 1: 30 points. 2: 10 points. 3: 20 points.

c) 1-3:

1: Expect this to take longer than the event's duration. 2: Two can play at this game. 3: Timing is one of the keys to Swingshot; wise contenders play this card.

SCORES 1: 10 points. 2: 20 points. 3: 30 points.

d) 1-3:

1: On the face of it SARACEN has the edge. 2: No doubt a good one if you can bluff convincingly. 3: Properly undertaken, this can leave SARACEN bemused.

SCORES 1: 10 points. 2: 20 points. 3: 30 points.

---

(6) PHOENIX
Swingshot is one of PHOENIX's best events.

PRINCIPAL OPTION a)
Intermediate Options 1-3:

1: PHOENIX became so good at this event by not allowing such liberties. 2: Some chance of succeeding, but remember her expertise in Swingshot. 3: This can be an unbeatable plan.

SCORES 1: 10 points. 2: 20 points. 3: 30 points.

b) 1-3:

1: Not a good choice where PHOENIX is concerned. 2: Let battle commence. 3: You have to risk her seeing through the pretence.

SCORES 1: 10 points. 2: 30 points. 3: 20 points.

c) 1-3:

1: Her stamina is high and you could come unstuck. 2: PHOENIX can power herself up to any level too. 3: A creditable plan.

SCORES 1: 20 points. 2: 10 points. 3: 30 points.

d) 1-3:

1: A slugging-match could ultimately favour you. 2: PHOENIX has seen all these tricks. 3: This one might befuddle her for a while.

SCORES 1: 30 points. 2: 10 points. 3: 20 points.

---

(7) HAWK
Swingshot is one of HAWK's best events.

PRINCIPAL OPTION a)
Intermediate Options 1-3:

Not likely to ruffle HAWK's feathers. 2: Pattern-breaking can serve you very nicely. 3: Let's say you stand a chance of achieving this.

SCORES 1: 10 points. 2: 30 points. 3: 20 points.

b) 1-3:

1: HAWK has overcome such strategies before. 2: The chances of him out-slugging you are perhaps too great. 3: Unpredictability can be a great asset.

SCORES 1: 10 points. 2: 20 points. 3: 30 points.

1-3:

1: HAWK is too well equipped to be beaten by this. 2: OK, he may not be able to match you every time. 3: Get that timing absolutely right and you're the champion.

SCORES 1: 10 points. 2: 20 points. 3: 30 points.

d) 1-3:

1: Not advisable as by no means a certainty you could overcome this Gladiator. 2: You could baffle him with this ploy. 3: Your best bet.

SCORES 1: 10 points. 2: 20 points. 3: 30 points.

---

(8) PANTHER
PRINCIPAL OPTION a)
Intermediate Options 1-3:

1: Could be she will swallow this, but don't count on it working each time. 2: PANTHER would probably block you anyway. 3: Quite possible if you go at it with dedication.

SCORES 1: 20 points. 2: 10 points. 3: 30 points.

b) 1-3:

1: Maybe a winner, at first. 2: Combat could land you the glittering prize. 3: PANTHER is too sussed to buy this one.

SCORES 1: 20 points. 2: 30 points. 3: 10 points.

c) 1-3:

1: She can be worn down, but maybe not in time to help you. 2: Her comparatively light weight would give you an advantage. 3: PANTHER is too alive to developments for this to happen.

SCORES 1: 20 points. 2: 30 points. 3: 10 points.

d) 1-3:

1: Don't go in half-heartedly and you can send her spiralling away. 2: PANTHER is too seasoned for this. 3: Some chance of this option working, but it is a fiddly plan to lay on this all-rounder.

SCORES 1: 30 points. 2: 10 points. 3: 20 points.

---

(9) WOLF
PRINCIPAL OPTION a)
Intermediate Options 1-3:

1: Some points possible but no guarantees. 2: You are trying to out-wolf WOLF. 3: Providing you aren't too exhausted it can be done.

SCORES 1: 20 points. 2: 10 points. 3: 30 points.

b) 1-3:

1: Worth a try, but WOLF will catch on fast. 2: Make it an ambush and it could be a bolt from the blue for him. 3: When it comes to guile, WOLF is hard to beat.

SCORES 1: 20 points. 2: 30 points. 3: 10 points.

c) 10-3:

1: A constant and hard onslaught would be necessary. 2: This would effectively play on the fact that he is one of the lighter male Gladiators. 3: His agility indicates a no-no.

SCORES 1: 20 points. 2: 30 points. 3: 10 points.

d) 1-3:

1: An option you should only go for if you have no other choice. 2: You can mess up his timing this way. 3: WOLF is going to be able to anticipate this.

SCORES 1: 10 points. 2: 30 points. 3: 20 points.

---

(10) FLAME

Swingshot is one of FLAME's best events.

PRINCIPAL OPTION a)
Intermediate Options 1-3:

1: FLAME can block this without too much trouble. 2: She will probably soon see what's going on. 3: FLAME is one of the stronger female Gladiators but get stuck in and it could pay dividends.

SCORES 1: 10 points. 2: 20 points. 3: 30 points.

b) 1-3:

1: Do this and you will discover why she is good at this event. 2: If you haven't spent too much energy before trying it, a confrontation can be your salvation. 3: Might work a few times, if your luck's in.

SCORES 1: 10 points. 2: 30 points. 3: 20 points.

c) 1-3:

1: FLAME can be extinguished this way. 2: She can do it too, at least as well. 3: If your timing is polished enough it can gain you some points.

SCORES 1: 30 points. 2: 10 points. 3: 20 points

d) 1-3:

1: If you are sure of your own strength a physical option like this can yield favourable results. 2: FLAME rarely mistimes, one of the reasons she does well on Swingshot. 3: Maybe a sound plan for one or two leaps.

SCORES 1: 30 points. 2: 10 points. 3: 20 points.

---

(11) COBRA
PRINCIPAL OPTION a)
Intermediate Options 1-3:

1: This must be best when up against an athlete like

COBRA. 2: COBRA will likely pile in anyway and spoil your plan. 3: Worst option against this bodybuilder and martial artist, particularly as you are tiring.

SCORES 1: 30 points. 2: 20 points. 3: 10 points.

b) 1-3:

1: An option that can harvest a rich crop of points. 2: Potentially a reckless move. 3: Could be effective for a limited period.

SCORES 1: 30 points. 2: 10 points. 3: 20 points.

c) 1-3:

1: He has too many tricks and too much martial experience to weaken. 2: Certainly it should make his jaw drop the first time, but subsequently? 3: Good acting ability and split-second timing could pull the points your way.

SCORES 1: 10 points. 2: 20 points. 3: 30 points.

d) 1-3:

1: The suspicion must be that this is exactly what COBRA wants. 2: His timing is good, so only a temporary advantage to you. 3: Befuddle him this way and those points are nearer.

SCORES 1: 10 points. 2: 20 points. 3: 30 points.

---

(12) LIGHTNING

Swingshot is one of LIGHTNING's best events.

PRINCIPAL OPTION a)
Intermediate Options 1-3:

1: If LIGHTNING fell for this tactic she wouldn't be a Swingshot champ. 2: Once or twice, yes; then it becomes less certain a ploy. 3: She is strong but small-framed when lined up against the other female Gladiators, so force is a viable option.

SCORES 1: 10 points. 2: 20 points. 3: 30 points.

b) 1-3:

1: This won't work for long against a Gladiator proficient at Swingshot. 2: Combat is the surest path. 3: LIGHTNING is not to be lightly distracted.

SCORES 1: 20 points. 2: 30 points. 3: 10 points.

c) 1-3:

1: You would have to get her to hang around for your attack, but it's worth it if you can. 2: LIGHTNING's athletic prowess would more than match your heroic leaps. 3: She strives to be in the right place at the right time.

SCORES 1: 30 points. 2: 10 points. 3: 20 points.

d) 1-3:

1: Get used to the idea of having to beat her off and you could find it's a good option. 2: Not with Swingshot ace LIGHTNING. 3: She'll catch on rapidly and be back to block you in a flash.

SCORES 1: 30 points. 2: 10 points. 3: 20 points.

(5) HANG TOUGH

Hang Tough is very accurately named. An aerial confrontation ten feet above the arena floor, it brings Gladiator and contender together in a one-on-one showdown. It is one of the most demanding of all the events in *Gladiators*.

You and your Gladiator opponent start on platforms at opposite sides of the playing area. The platforms are fifty feet apart. In between are ten rows of hanging rings, one every four feet. The central row of rings, coloured blue, is classed as the scoring zone.

If you can swing across to the Gladiator's platform in one minute you score ten points. Should you not manage this, there are five points to be gained if you are still clinging to the rings in the blue scoring zone when the whistle blows. This is called hanging tough.

What you have to avoid is your Gladiator zeroing in on you, ripping you from the rings and sending you crashing to the floor below.

This is a truly punishing event. It requires outstanding upper body and arm strength, and also the agility needed to stay out of your opponent's way.

PRINCIPAL OPTIONS

Do you:

a) *Take the bull by the horns and head straight for the opposition's platform in an all-out frontal assault?*

b) *Meet the Gladiator on the rings, counting on your grip being more tenacious and that your opponent will be the one to hurtle to the floor?*

c) *Go directly to the blue scoring zone, determined to hang tough until the whistle sounds, clinging tenaciously to the rings no matter what your opponent does?*

d) *Gamble on tiring out the Gladiator by leading him or her on a merry dance around the rings until you see an opening to either your opponent's platform or the blue scoring zone?*

INTERMEDIATE OPTIONS

P.O. a) What happens:

The Gladiator whose platform you are storming meets force with force and defends the base by furiously tearing into you.

In response, you:

1. Try to give as good as you get and engage him/her in a battle designed to make your opponent lose his/her grip on the rings.

2. Disentangle yourself from the Gladiator and test whether your speed is great enough to leave him/her behind, then mount another charge at the platform.

3. Do your best to edge toward the blue scoring zone with the aim of still being there when time is called.

P.O. b) What happens:

You and the Gladiator are too well matched — he/she sticks to the rings like super-glue as time trickles away.

In response, you:

1. Take the bold step of hanging by only one ring so you have a hand as well as your lower body to use against your challenger.

2. Discard the notion of overpowering your opponent, break away and try to shake him/her off with a burst of speed.

3. Back off and head for the blue scoring zone, then suddenly change direction and go all-out for the undefended platform.

P.O. c) What happens:

The Gladiator subjects you to a punishing rain of blows from the lower body, and also rapidly alternates the arm he/she is hanging from in order to add a hand to the attack, wearing down your ability to stay aloft.

In response, you:

1. Put aside the idea of hanging passively, absorbing everything your opponent can throw at you, and put up a spirited counter-attack.

2. Abandon the blue scoring zone and try to out-speed the Gladiator back to his/her open platform.

3. Bide your time until your opponent is in the process of changing the hand he or she is hanging from, then hit your enemy with everything you have while he/she is most vulnerable.

P.O. d) What happens:

Your Gladiator opponent moves from ring to ring with dexterity, consistently barring your path to both the platform and the scoring zone.

In response, you:

1. Zap your way directly over to the Gladiator and unleash a blistering attack meant to put him/her off the rings and out of the event.

2. Carry on with your original plan until the last few seconds, then bank on being able to make a determined dash for the Gladiator's platform.

3. Stop hanging around and single-mindedly concentrate on a do or die race for the scoring zone.

Event Five
HANG TOUGH
SCORE CHECK

(1) SHADOW

Hang Tough is one of SHADOW's best events.

PRINCIPAL OPTION a)
Intermediate Options 1-3:

1: Team leader SHADOW's cool, super-fitness and strength make this the least advisable option. 2: Getting away is by no means certain, but a charge at his base could catch him off-guard. 3: This crafty move, coupled with tenacity, is best.

SCORES 1: 10 points. 2: 20 points. 3: 30 points.

b) 1-3:

1: Too likely you'll be the one doing the hurtling. 2: Moderate chance of succeeding. 3: Punishing but potentially most profitable.

SCORES 1: 10 points. 2: 20 points. 3: 30 points.

c) 1-3:

1: A mistake to get hung up on this option. 2: Possible, if you aren't too exhausted to really *move*. 3: Even SHADOW could find this hard to counter.

SCORES 1: 10 points. 2: 20 points. 3: 30 points.

d) 1-3:

1: The kind of trap SHADOW lays for unwary opponents. 2: Requires element of surprise, otherwise quite sound. 3: Only if you do it early in the event when you still have strength left. And still doubtful...

---

(2) **SCORPIO**
PRINCIPAL OPTION a)
Intermediate Options 1-3:

1: Yes, if you can deliver a stinging attack. 2: No to both stages of this plan. 3: The flaw here is that SCORPIO may have the edge when it comes to edging.

SCORES 1: 30 points. 2: 10 points. 3: 20 points.

b) 1-3:

1: SCORPIO's dexterity makes it hazardous. 2: Small chance with this Gladiator. 3: If convincing and fast, yes.

SCORES 1: 20 points. 2: 10 points. 3: 30 points.

c) 1-3:

1: Don't get too hung up on this going your way. 2: You would be up against all of SCORPIO's best qualities. 3: This can make a drop-out of her.

SCORES 1: 20 points. 2: 10 points. 3: 30 points.

d) 1-3:

1: Don't leave it until you have depleted your energy and it could be goodbye SCORPIO. 2: Can be done if you have enough zip left. 3: She is a superior athlete and this is her thing.

SCORES 1: 30 points. 2: 20 points. 3: 10 points.

---

(3) **WARRIOR**
PRINCIPAL OPTION a)
Intermediate Options 1-3:

1: With mighty WARRIOR, too good a chance of finding yourself on your back. 2: His immense weight could slow him in the chase. 3: Wisp of a chance of pulling this off.

    SCORES   1: 10 points.   2: 30 points.   3: 20 points.

b) 1-3:

1: You need a firm grip when WARRIOR's facing you. 2: You can make it. 3: Might surprise him enough.

    SCORES   1: 10 points.   2: 30 points.   3: 20 points.

c) 1-3:

1: He can put too much power into those blows. 2: Give it your all and success is in sight. 3: A slim chance.

    SCORES   1: 10 points.   2: 30 points.   3: 20 points.

d) 1-3:

1: He's not going to hang around and take this. 2: WARRIOR can be out-paced if you don't telegraph it. 3: A fighting chance.

    SCORES   1: 10 points.   2: 30 points.   3: 20 points.

---

(4) JET

Hang Tough is one of JET's best events.

PRINCIPAL OPTION a)
Intermediate Options 1-3:

1: Don't delay your assault, use every ounce of strength, and gravity could take her. 2: JET will zoom in on you. 3: Only if she lets you get there.

    SCORES   1: 30 points.   2: 10 points.   3: 20 points.

b) 1-3:

1: This could give you the edge you need. 2: JET-power will probably overtake you. 3: Even with luck, only maybe.

SCORES 1: 30 points. 2: 10 points. 3: 20 points.

c) 1-3:

1: She is a spirited fighter too, remember. 2: Will only get you a demonstration of JET's expertise at this event. 3: Making this decision early on while your strength is still there will put JET into a nose-dive.

SCORES 1: 20 points. 2: 10 points. 3: 30 points.

d) 1-3:

1: Best chance of a result in your favour. 2: The unexpected element could bring this off. 3: More likely die than do for you.

SCORES 1: 30 points. 2: 20 points. 3: 10 points.

---

(5) SARACEN
Hang Tough is one of SARACEN's best events.

PRINCIPAL OPTION a)
Intermediate Options 1-3:

1: Your grip on reality may be weaker. 2: A positive course if you can bring off all three stages. 3: A prudent compromise.

SCORES 1: 10 points. 2: 20 points. 3: 30 points.

b) 1-3:

1: Bold enough that it might just work. 2: Too many imponderables. 3: High-risk option needing flair to achieve.

SCORES 1: 30 points. 2: 10 points. 3: 20 points.

c) 1-3:

1: No better than a maybe option. 2: SARACEN would thank you for being so rash. 3: Of the options offered, the one you stand to succeed with.

SCORES 1: 20 points. 2: 10 points. 3: 30 points.

d) 1-3:

1: Only if *really* blistering. 2: SARACEN won't tire, but the surprise turn could throw him. 3: Watch him go.

SCORES 1: 20 points. 2: 30 points. 3: 10 points.

---

(6) PHOENIX
PRINCIPAL OPTION a)
Intermediate Options 1-3:

1: Light but tenacious PHOENIX *could* be overcome this way. 2: Her speed is telling. 3: If you really can hang with the toughest, yes.

SCORES 1: 20 points. 2: 10 points. 3: 30 points.

b) 1-3:

1: If you have the nerve and energy. 2: PHOENIX can be relied upon to dog you all the way. 3: More no than yes.

SCORES 1: 30 points. 2: 10 points. 3: 20 points.

c) 1-3:

1: Counter like mad and ground her. 2: Come, come now. 3: Possible, but involves being quicker and more agile than she.

SCORES 1: 30 points. 2: 10 points. 3: 20 points.

d) 1-3:

1: Give no quarter, watch her fall. 2: A significant risk of

75

being caught. 3: PHOENIX is too light and fast.

SCORES 1: 30 points. 2: 20 points. 3: 10 points.

---

(7) HAWK

Hang Tough is one of HAWK's best events.

PRINCIPAL OPTION a)
Intermediate Options 1-3:

1: HAWK does not often let go. 2: Maybe, at best. 3: Stealth and stubbornness will pay.

SCORES 1: 10 points. 2: 20 points. 3: 30 points.

b) 1-3:

1: A daring move of this kind could clip HAWK's wings. 2: He'll swoop in for the kill. 3: Don't overlook his canniness in this event.

SCORES 1: 30 points. 2: 10 points. 3: 20 points.

c) 1-3:

1: If spirited really describes your response, there's a chance. 2: Best way of putting yourself at his mercy. 3: Strike like quicksilver and he could flutter away.

SCORES 1: 20 points. 2: 10 points. 3: 30 points.

d) 1-3:

1: Take an early shower. 2: Your chance to bloody his beak. 3: Might put HAWK in a flap.

SCORES 1: 10 points. 2: 30 points. 3: 20 points.

---

(8) PANTHER
PRINCIPAL OPTION a)
Intermediate Options 1-3:

1: You can draw PANTHER's claws this way. 2: Her excellent physical condition spells no. 3: You might be able to Hang Tough.

    SCORES 1: 30 points. 2: 10 points. 3: 20 points.

b) 1-3:

1: An extra hand can make light work of PANTHER. 2: She's bound to bound along with you. 3: Perilous, given her agility.

    SCORES 1: 30 points. 2: 10 points. 3: 20 points.

c) 1-3:

1: A purr-fect ploy. 2: Only could be. 3: Feline fleetness stacks the odds against you.

    SCORES 1: 30 points. 2: 20 points. 3: 10 points.

d) 1-3:

1: Zap her good and watch the fur fly. 2: Finely judged timing and high speed necessary. 3: Good chance she'll strike before you make it.

    SCORES 1: 30 points. 2: 20 points. 3: 10 points.

---

(9) WOLF
Hang Tough is one of WOLF's best events.

PRINCIPAL OPTION a)
Intermediate Options 1-3:

1: Yes, but a hard slugging needed. 2: Possible for WOLF to trip you at any stage. 3: WOLF is the master craftyman.

    SCORES 1: 30 points. 2: 20 points. 3: 10 points.

b) 1-3:

1: An audacious move that can bring him to heel. 2: Not against lopping WOLF. 3: He is capable of sniffing this one out unless you're careful.

SCORES 1: 30 points. 2: 10 points. 3: 20 points.

c) 1-3:

1: How much time remains could be the crucial factor. 2: WOLF will romp along beside you. 3: He is at a definite disadvantage hanging from just one paw.

SCORES 1: 20 points. 2: 10 points. 3: 30 points.

d) 1-3:

1: Go in swinging and it's a dog-gone victory for you. 2: Too many opportunities for WOLF to bite back. 3: Ignore his agility and you might hear the whistle from below.

SCORES 1: 30 points. 2: 10 points. 3: 20 points.

---

(10) FLAME

Hang Tough is one of FLAME's best events.

PRINCIPAL OPTION a)
Intermediate Options 1-3:

1: If you can deliver a battering around her extended reach FLAME can be put out. 2: Exactly the way she wins at this event herself. 3: A scalding option but survivable.

SCORES 1: 30 points. 2: 10 points. 3: 20 points.

b) 1-3:

1: An additional weapon can tell against her. 2: Put together the following two words – 'definitely' and 'not'. 3: Might dampen her enthusiasm.

SCORES 1: 30 points. 2: 10 points. 3: 20 points.

c) 1-3:

1: Capable of quenching her burning ambitions. 2: She simmers with speed. 3: Could go one way or the other, in your case possibly down.

SCORES 1: 30 points. 2: 10 points. 3: 20 points.

d) 1-3:

1: Has the potential to smoke her out. 2: FLAME does have an athletic advantage, it must be said. 3: She's crackingly good at speed tests.

SCORES 1: 30 points. 2: 20 points. 3: 10 points.

---

(11) COBRA
Hang Tough is one of COBRA's best events.

PRINCIPAL OPTION a)
Intermediate Options 1-3:

1: Could foil the coiled one. 2: COBRA's too good a mover on those rings. 3: If you can get to the blues you have a fighting chance of staying there.

SCORES 1: 20 points. 2: 10 points. 3: 30 points.

b) 1-3:

1: If you make it unexpected and don't hold back. 2: Old snake hips can out-slither you. 3: Just a chance.

SCORES 1: 30 points. 2: 10 points. 3: 20 points.

c) 1-3:

1: A full-scale attack can win the battle. 2: Extremely unlikely. 3: Only assuming COBRA drops his guard long enough.

SCORES 1: 30 points. 2: 10 points. 3: 20 points.

d) 1-3:

1: Will work if he doesn't slide away. 2: Hang Tough champ COBRA might have encountered this move before. 3: Not with this calibre of Gladiator.

SCORES 1: 30 points. 2: 20 points. 3: 10 points.

---

(12) LIGHTNING

One of LIGHTNING's best events.

PRINCIPAL OPTION a)
Intermediate Options 1-3:

1: Has potential to make LIGHTNING bolt. 2: She conducts herself too well. 3: Bear in mind she has already seen most of the tricks.

SCORES 1: 30 points. 2: 10 points. 3: 20 points.

b) 1-3:

1: Could get grim, but perseverance can snatch victory. 2: She'll be ahead of you in a flash. 3: Would have to be a shocking move on your part.

SCORES 1: 30 points. 2: 10 points. 3: 20 points.

c) 1-3:

1: A long bout is predicted. 2: LIGHTNING will streak there before you. 3: Gives you a winning edge.

SCORES 1: 20 points. 2: 10 points. 3: 30 points.

d) 1-3:

1: A thundering attack can dislodge her. 2: Doubtful, but not entirely out of the question. 3: Prepare for a bolt from the blue.

SCORES 1: 30 points. 2: 20 points. 3: 10 points.

(6) DUEL

No holds are barred in this modern day version of the joust.

You and the Gladiator each stand on four foot diameter platforms twelve feet above the playing floor. The platforms are sixteen inches apart. Both you and your opponent are armed with seven foot long pugil sticks. Pugil sticks are fighting staffs, both ends of which are covered in hard-impact rubber. Despite the protective helmets you and your gladiator are wearing, these sticks can still deliver a very nasty jolt.

The object of Duel is simple: you must knock the Gladiator off his or her platform without being knocked off yourself in the process. Neither of you is allowed to step over onto the other's platform. You cannot drop your pugil stick. If you do either of these you are disqualified.

Ten points are scored if you topple your Gladiator opponent from his/her platform. You get five points for remaining on the platform for the thirty seconds duration of the event.

PRINCIPAL OPTIONS

Do you:

a) *Go in fighting as hard as you can to topple the Gladiator from his/her platform?*

b) *Firmly anchor yourself to your platform, use the pugil stick to fend off your opponent's blows defensively, and strive to stay put for the duration of the event?*

c) *Constantly taunt your opponent, and make feinting moves with your pugil stick in the hope they will forget themselves, step over onto your platform and be disqualified?*

d) *Work hard to knock the pugil stick out of the Gladiator's grasp, leading to your opponent's disqualification?*

INTERMEDIATE OPTIONS

P.O. a) What happens:

The Gladiator you are opposing seems immovable, soaking-up everything you can throw.

In response, you:

1. Change your priority and set yourself the task of simply remaining on your platform until the event is over.

2. Call upon whatever reserves of energy you have left and increase the ferocity of your assault.

3. Devote yourself to parting the Gladiator from his/her pugil stick in order that your enemy be drummed out of the game.

P.O. b) What happens:

The constant battering your opposer is delivering to you is starting to make a defensive strategy look impractical.

In response, you:

1. Remain convinced your enemy cannot keep up the furious onslaught for much longer and become even more set on your idea of weathering the storm until the whistle blows.

2. Decide the time has come for an offensive, throwing yourself into hitting back as hard as you are able.

3. Fight back, but try to make your blows count by carefully targeting them against your opponent's most vulnerable areas.

P.O. c) What happens:

Your antagonist does not seem to be taking the bait and refuses to be drawn over onto your platform.

In response, you:

1. Take a more head-on approach and go in for the kill, hoping that by changing tack in this way your opponent will be thrown off balance enough so that you can deliver some crucial blows.

2. Step up your policy of provocation, and feigning moves, in the belief that the Gladiator will lose his/her cool and invade your platform.

3. Fall back into a defensive mode and just try to hang on until the game finishes.

P.O. d) What happens:

Gladiator and pugil stick seem inseparable, and are being used against you with devastating effect.

In response, you:

1. Give up trying to part the Gladiator from his/her stick and direct your efforts toward hitting in what you hope will be more sensitive areas.

2. Make several swings at your opponent which you know will pass over his/her head without connecting, then put your all into a swing directed squarely at the upper body, on the basis that this will surprise and topple the opponent.

3. Fall back into a defensive stance and try drinking up the buffeting as it comes at you until the allotted time is up.

Sixth Event
DUEL
SCORE CHECK

(1) SHADOW

Duel is one of SHADOW's best events.

PRINCIPAL OPTION a)
Intermediate Options 1-3:

1: Having shot your bolt, best to lay low. 2: Not probable if you haven't managed to best SHADOW by now. 3: SHADOW's grasp is not insubstantial.

SCORES 1: 30 points. 2: 20 points. 3: 10 points.

b) 1-3:

1: You've got this far; hang on. 2: At this stage it's too late for SHADOW boxing. 3: This assumes his vulnerable areas are exposed.

SCORES 1: 30 points. 2: 10 points. 3: 20 points.

c) 1-3:

1: Perhaps the surprise of you changing strategy will tell. 2: SHADOW does not win constantly at Duel by losing his cool. 3: Best of the available options.

SCORES 1: 20 points. 2: 10 points. 3: 30 points.

d) 1-3:

1: Depends perhaps too much on an opening. 2: SHADOW is unlikely to buy this trick. 3: The seconds will crawl, but your best choice here.

SCORES 1: 20 points. 2: 10 points. 3: 30 points.

(2) SCORPIO

PRINCIPAL OPTION a)
Intermediate Options 1-3:

1: Not wise to throw away what may have been gained. 2: If you have reserves of strength, a sensible step. 3: It could be worth switching to this option.

SCORES 1: 10 points. 2: 30 points. 3: 20 points.

b) 1-3:

1: Could be a reasonable assumption. 2: SCORPIO may be tired enough by now to make this effective. 3: She is going to defend herself.

SCORES 1: 20 points. 2: 30 points. 3: 10 points.

c) 1-3:

1: You could crush this bug. 2: She is too clear-headed to step over. 3: You probably could, but isn't it a bit passive?

SCORES 1: 30 points. 2: 10 points. 3: 20 points.

d) 1-3:

1: SCORPIO may leave openings, but don't depend on it. 2: Not a bad way of finishing the match. 3: This negates all your earlier efforts.

SCORES 1: 20 points. 2: 30 points. 3: 10 points.

---

(3) WARRIOR

Duel is one of WARRIOR's best events.

PRINCIPAL OPTION a)
Intermediate Options 1-3:

1: Always take cover in an avalanche. 2: Unlikely to make too much of a dent. 3: Little prospect of working.

SCORES 1: 30 points. 2: 10 points. 3: 20 points.

b) 1-3:

1: WARRIOR *might* tire, eventually. 2: Water off a duck's back. 3: The best of three difficult options when it comes to this Gladiator.

SCORES 1: 20 points. 2: 10 points. 3: 30 points.

c) 1-3:

1: You're joking, of course. 2: WARRIOR would take a lot of goading. 3: Gritting your teeth and taking it is your way out.

SCORES 1: 10 points. 2: 20 points. 3: 30 points.

d) 1-3:

1: Does WARRIOR have any sensitive spots? 2: A small chance of this option coming off. 3: A wise contender waits for the whistle.

SCORES 1: 10 points. 2: 20 points. 3: 30 points.

---

(4) JET

Duel is one of JET's best events.

PRINCIPAL OPTION a)
Intermediate Options 1-3:

1: She could wear down but you've lost precious points. 2: Could be worth putting your back into this. 3: A strategy with much to commend it.

SCORES 1: 10 points. 2: 20 points. 3: 30 points.

b) 1-3:

1: You can probably withstand JET's thrusting assault. 2: She may have used up enough energy for this to hit home.

3: JET is supreme at blocking blows.

   SCORES 1: 20 points. 2: 30 points. 3: 10 points.

c) 1-3:

1: Stepping up your attack this way can be rewarding. 2: JET won't be provoked. 3: You probably will hang on to the bitter end.

   SCORES 1: 30 points. 2: 10 points. 3: 20 points.

d) 1-3:

1: Her blocking abilities militate against this. 2: A clever strategy which could shoot down this JET. 3: Possible, if you don't mind a headache.

   SCORES 1: 10 points. 2: 30 points. 3: 20 points.

---

(5) SARACEN
PRINCIPAL OPTION a)
Intermediate Options 1-3:

1: SARACEN will see this as weakness and renew his efforts. 2: Chipping away could yield a result. 3: Judge the force and angle of your blows and the stick could go flying.

   SCORES 1: 10 points. 2: 20 points. 3: 30 points.

b) 1-3:

1: Note that SARACEN can whip up quite a storm. 2: Too late for this. 3: A telling strike is possible, particularly if the Gladiator has become over-confident.

   SCORES 1: 20 points. 2: 10 points. 3: 30 points.

c) 1-3:

1: Well worth going for this. 2: SARACEN is the steady

type. 3: Feasible, but he is relentless.

SCORES 1: 30 points. 2: 10 points. 3: 20 points.

d) 1-3:

1: If he thinks he has you beaten the shock of you switching strategies might leave him unprotected. 2: A winner if cunningly undertaken. 3: You're inviting defeat.

SCORES 1: 20 points. 2: 30 points. 3: 10 points.

---

(6) PHOENIX
PRINCIPAL OPTION a)
Intermediate Options 1-3:

1: Hanging on is possible, but this sends a defeatist signal. 2: Push her for all you're worth. 3: PHOENIX and stick tend to be inseparable.

SCORES 1: 20 points. 2: 30 points. 3: 10 points.

b) 1-3:

1: You could be right. 2: Crash into her and she may not rise again. 3: PHOENIX covers herself too well.

SCORES 1: 20 points. 2: 30 points. 3: 10 points.

c) 1-3:

1: Be alert for openings and points could come your way. 2: She might be tempted over if you irritate her enough. 3: Plucky PHOENIX could take this as a signal to hand out a further pasting.

SCORES 1: 30 points. 2: 20 points. 3: 10 points.

d) 1-3:

1: Only if PHOENIX displays over-confidence and leaves herself open. 2: These kind of tactics can garner points.

3: The passive message this sends could encourage her all the more.

SCORES 1: 20 points. 2: 30 points. 3: 10 points.

---

(7) HAWK
PRINCIPAL OPTION a)
Intermediate Options 1-3

1: You can stay put, but why give up? 2: Increase the pressure and the prize gets nearer. 3: HAWK has too tight a grip.

SCORES 1: 20 points. 2: 30 points. 3: 10 points.

b) 1-3:

1: This looks like apathy on your part. 2: Could set him back on his heels. 3: Perhaps, but there may be none available to target.

SCORES 1: 10 points. 2: 30 points. 3: 20 points.

c) 1-3:

1: HAWK could be wrong-footed. 2: He won't be foolish enough to come over. 3: You could still be upright for the whistle.

SCORES 1: 30 points. 2: 10 points. 3: 20 points.

d) 1-3:

1: HAWK is unruffled. 2: Confusion can be a good weapon. 3: An invitation for further attacks.

SCORES 1: 10 points. 2: 30 points. 3: 20 points.

---

(8) PANTHER
PRINCIPAL OPTION a)

Intermediate Options 1-3:

1: PANTHER won't go any easier on you though. 2: No, this feline protects her den. 3: Well-aimed hits can de-stick her.

    SCORES 1: 20 points. 2: 10 points. 3: 30 points.

b) 1-3:

1: OK, but why not go on the offensive? 2: The time is right for this. 3: PANTHER is too well defended.

    SCORES 1: 20 points. 2: 30 points. 3: 10 points.

c) 1-3:

1: Your crucial option. 2: PANTHER won't be put off her stroke. 3: Possible but passive.

    SCORES 1: 30 points. 2: 10 points. 3: 20 points.

d) 1-3:

1: Too difficult to get through. 2: Weaving a spell and walloping can fell the cat. 3: Her battering can be absorbed.

    SCORES 1: 10 points. 2: 30 points. 3: 20 points.

---

(9) WOLF
PRINCIPAL OPTION a)
Intermediate Options 1-3:

1: If you don't mind being a sitting target. 2: Pushing it as far as you can, can see WOLF off. 3: He won't lose his stick.

    SCORES 1: 20 points. 2: 30 points. 3: 10 points.

b) 1-3:

1: Maybe WOLF will flag. 2: Going in with a grievance

can come up trumps. 3: WOLF will not let your stick through.

SCORES 1: 20 points. 2: 30 points. 3: 10 points.

c) 1-3:

1: There is a better than good chance that you can ensnare WOLF like this. 2: Keeping his cool helps make WOLF a Duel champion. 3: You can, but a more positive approach could be preferable.

SCORES 1: 30 points. 2: 10 points. 3: 20 points.

d) 1-3:

1: You'll be lucky to have the opportunity. 2: A smashing option. 3: Too pessimistic a way of dealing with the situation.

SCORES 1: 20 points. 2: 30 points. 3: 10 points.

---

(10) FLAME

Duel is one of FLAME's best events.

PRINCIPAL OPTION a)
Intermediate Options 1-3:

1: Weathering FLAME's onslaught is not impossible. 2: You have nothing to lose and all to gain. 3: It would be a flaming miracle.

SCORES 1: 20 points. 2: 30 points. 3: 10 points.

b) 1-3:

1: Yes, but you could do better with a more active approach. 2: Dedicated combat can dampen FLAME. 3: Not likely she will leave you an opening.

SCORES 1: 20 points. 2: 30 points. 3: 10 points.

c) 1-3:

1: A roaring attack can reduce FLAME to ashes. 2: Her expertise at Duel was gained through keeping calm. 3: Yes, but not as profitable as positive action.

SCORES 1: 30 points. 2: 10 points. 3: 20 points.

d) 1-3:

1: Good thinking but those sensitive areas may be hidden. 2: This strategy can overwhelm FLAME's defences. 3: She may step-up her attack in response.

SCORES 1: 20 points. 2: 30 points. 3: 10 points.

---

(11) COBRA
Duel is one of COBRA's best events.

PRINCIPAL OPTION a)
Intermediate Options 1-3:

1: COBRA will move in to finish you. 2: It would take some ferocity. 3: Risky, but best available option.

SCORES 1: 10 points. 2: 20 points. 3: 30 points.

b) 1-3:

1: Could be well worth the effort. 2: COBRA stays icy cool. 3: You might do better with another option.

SCORES 1: 30 points. 2: 10 points. 3: 20 points.

c) 1-3:

1: COBRA triumphs at Duel by not falling for these ploys. 2: Just maybe. 3: Sitting tight could be your best option in this situation.

SCORES 1: 10 points. 2: 20 points. 3: 30 points.

d) 1-3:

1: You would be very fortunate to get through COBRA's defences. 2: Needs panache, but it can deliver the goods. 3: COBRA's buffeting will doubtless increase.

SCORES 1: 20 points. 2: 30 points. 3: 10 points.

---

(12) LIGHTNING
PRINCIPAL OPTION a)
Intermediate Options 1-3:

1: You'll probably still be there, but you could gain more with another option. 2: Summon up the power and charge in. 3: LIGHTNING won't give it up.

SCORES 1: 20 points. 2: 30 points. 3: 10 points.

b) 1-3:

1: A reasonable supposition. 2: Pummelling LIGHTNING can light up your chances. 3: Small chance of delivering those telling blows.

SCORES 1: 20 points. 2: 30 points. 3: 10 points.

c) 1-3:

1: This can earth LIGHTNING's strikes. 2: She won't put her cool to one side. 3: It can be done.

SCORES 1: 30 points. 2: 10 points. 3: 20 points.

d) 1-3:

1: In the fury of battle this can be a fine option. 2: Feigning moves can sometimes pay off. 3: Drinking it up is all very well, but you could do better with another course of action.

SCORES 1: 30 points. 2: 20 points. 3: 10 points.

(7) ELIMINATOR

You have now arrived at the last and possibly most difficult event – ELIMINATOR.

This time you are on your own. ELIMINATOR, which takes the form of an incredibly tough obstacle course, does not include a Gladiator opponent. How well you do in it depends on the score accumulated up to this point, because you will be gambling those points on the outcome.

You are about to have five chances to increase the total score achieved on the previous events. But you could as easily lose points or end up with the same score. It all depends on the dice. At each of the following stages of ELIMINATOR you will throw the dice to see whether your score goes up by 30 points, down by 30 points or stays the same.

Let's assume you enter stage one of ELIMINATOR with a total of 100 points. Throw the dice. If the numbers 1 or 2 come up you *deduct* 30 points, reducing your total to 70. If the numbers 2 or 3 come up your score *remains the same*, 100. If the numbers 5 or 6 come up you *add* 30 points, making your total 130. Repeat this through all five stages, keeping a running total.

So make a note of your overall score and have your dice ready.

Stage One

You begin ELIMINATOR by climbing a sixteen foot cargo net which takes you to a slide. This sweeps down to a scramble sheet. You then crawl twelve feet up this to a platform.

Now throw the dice to see if your score goes up 30 points, down 30 points, or stays the same.

Stage Two

Male and female contenders briefly part at this point. The women have to use an overhead ladder to traverse a sixteen foot gap and arrive at another platform. The men must pedal across to the platform using an overhead handbike.

Throw the dice and discover whether you score goes up, down or remains the same.

Stage Three

Reunited, the contenders move from the platform to run across a rolling beam, a spinning cylinder which makes it very difficult to keep your balance. It brings you to a twenty-four foot cargo net connected to an aerial platform. Tethered to the platform is a zip line running the ninety foot length of the arena and ending on a mat.

Throw the dice.

Stage Four

You now hit the travelator. This device is like a flat escalator, similar to the people-transporters used in airports. The devilish twist here is that it is going the wrong way! After all the tiring feats you have just performed the travelator can be quite an ordeal.

Throw the dice.

Stage Five

There is one more part to this stamina-sapping event. At the end of the travelator you mount a rope swing and zip over to a paper burst. Breaking through this completes the course.

Throw the dice.

The next section assesses your total score.

HOW YOU SCORED

If you scored up to 350 points:

You fought well but with not enough attention paid to strategy. There has also been a tendency to avoid strength confrontations. You ignored meeting the Gladiators head-on too often, and this course could have paid dividends.

Adopting a bolder, more daring approach can be to your advantage. Think carefully about the strategies you use when entering the events. Do not be afraid to try matching your strength against the Gladiator if, in your estimation, there is a chance of scoring additional points.

Work on building your confidence and body strength. Bear this in mind and you should do better the next time you meet the Gladiators.

If you scored up to 600 points:

This is a very commendable performance, and by and large you have taken sensible options. But you have occasionally picked a reckless course where a more cautious one would have served you better.

To improve your score next time do study the abilities of your Gladiator opponents very carefully in order to help you make the correct decisions. Do not overly rely on options requiring strength. Sometimes a strategic or defensive course of action can be wiser.

If you scored over 600 points:

Congratulations – you are a Gladiator Champion!

You have studied your opponents' abilities very closely and applied your mind to the task of choosing the right options against them. Your choice of offensive, defensive and strategic options has been well suited to the individual event and Gladiator.